SCOOP OF PLAYS

Paul Groves
John Griffin
Nigel Grimshaw

Contents

The Strange Girl

A ghostly school play

The Pond

Have you ever found anything odd on a rubbish dump?
Sue, Colin and Bob do.

Sherlock Holmes and the Great Trouser Mystery

Where have all the trousers of the male staff of
St Olave's Comprehensive gone? Can Sherlock Holmes
solve the mystery? Are you stupid enough to read this
play?

Horror at Hellfire Hall

CAST:	**Sir Basil Orfle** **Lady Jezebel Orfle** **Lawyer Parchment** **Judd Dullard** **Jennifer Sweetly** **Mr McFang** **Mrs McFang** **Sebastian Doome** **Widow Spyder**
SCENE:	*The drawing room at Hellfire Hall*
	Lawyer Parchment is talking to Sir Basil and Lady Orfle.

Sir Basil Curses and damnation! Parchment! You don't mean—! You can't mean—!

Parchment I do and I can, Sir Basil. There is no doubt about it in law.

Lady Orfle This viper – this Jennifer Sweetly – is true mistress of Hellfire Hall?

Parchment Indeed she is, my lady. The will – lost for years – tells us so.

Lady Orfle And she is coming here today? To live? For good?

Parchment After many years of poverty, she is looking forward to it, ma'am.

Sir Basil Looking forward to it, is she? The devil! Looking forward to lording it over us, eh?

Parchment Oh no, sir. She is a gentle creature. She is looking forward to living here with you in love and friendship. She is a harmless, trusting child.

Lady Orfle Pah! I hate harmless, trusting children!

Sir Basil And I loathe gentle creatures!

Parchment You are well known for it, sir. But there is nothing to be done. The law is the law. I am sorry.

Sir Basil Sorry! You dare to say you're sorry, you rogue! You will be sorry, you blackguard! Sorry! Pah!

Lady Orfle	Now, now, my dear. Calm yourself. It has been a shock. You must pardon him, Parchment.
Parchment	I do readily, my lady.
Sir Basil	Yes. I was hasty, Parchment. Forgive me. And – er – leave the will on the table there, will you? We'd like to study it.
Parchment	Gladly, sir. It is – after all – only a copy. I have the original in my safe-keeping.

He goes out.

Sir Basil	Curses! We cannot destroy the will.
Lady Orfle	We must.
Sir Basil	We can't. Let me think. Ah! Summon the servants.

Lady Orfle pulls a bellcord. Doome, Widow Spyder, Judd Dullard and Mr and Mrs McFang come in.

Doome	You rang for us, sir.
Sir Basil	I did. And I'll come straight to the point. Hellfire Hall is to have a new mistress. Lady Orfle and I will no longer rule here.
Mr McFang	A new mistress!
Doome	You don't mean—?
Sir Basil	I do mean, Doome.
Lady Orfle	A silly, soft-hearted girl is to take over the reins.
Doome	Then – there will be changes.
Mr McFang	Changes?
Sir Basil	Yes, McFang. Big changes. She will not like the Thing in the Cellar. It may have to go.
Mrs McFang	No!
Widow Spyder	Not the Thing in the Cellar, sir!
Sir Basil	Yes. And, probably, the Devil Plant in the Tower Room too!
Widow Spyder	The Devil Plant! She couldn't! Are you certain, sir?
Sir Basil	Nothing in this world is certain, Widow Spyder. I have a plan.
Mr McFang	Ah! Good! A plan!
Doome	I thought you would have, sir.
Sir Basil	If this girl – this Jennifer Sweetly – were to

	meet with an accident . . . .
Doome	A serious accident, sir?
Sir Basil	A fatal accident, Doome.
Lady Orfle	Then we, as her relatives, would inherit Hellfire Hall and all would be well. My dear, how clever!
Mr McFang	Devilish smart, sir!
Widow Spyder	Fiendishly cunning!
Sir Basil	Thank you, McFang. Thank you, Widow Spyder. We shall, of course, need your help.
Mr McFang	You can count on the missus and me, sir.
Doome	And I can speak for Widow Spyder and myself. Rely on us, sir.
Sir Basil	Good. And you – you have not spoken. Who is this fellow?
Doome	The new man, sir. Name of Judd Dullard. He's the replacement for Jacob Slyme.
Sir Basil	Slyme?
Doome	The Thing in the Cellar got him. Ate him, sir, if you remember.
Sir Basil	Ah yes, of course. Most amusing. Well – Dullard – are you with us?
Dullard	You what?
Sir Basil	Will you help us, you dolt?
Dullard	Eh?
Lady Orfle	He's not very bright, is he Doome?
Sir Basil	Hardly human.
Doome	I'm sorry, Sir Basil. He was the best I could get. None of the villagers want to work at Hellfire Hall, as you know.
Sir Basil	Never mind. He'll take orders, no doubt. And – if not – eh, Doome?
Doome	Quite so, Sir Basil. If he doesn't come up to scratch, the Thing in the Cellar or the Devil Plant will be glad of him. Always ready for a snack, they are.
Mr McFang	Heh! Heh! Heh!
Sir Basil	Enough of the jesting. Let's get back to Miss Sweetly. Who's going to see that she has her accident?
Mrs McFang	Ooh! Me, please, sir.
Doome	I am the butler, sir. It's only right—
Widow Spyder	No, no, let me!
Mr McFang	I'd be best at it, sir.

Sir Basil	You probably would. You stay here and I'll tell you what to do. The rest of you – clear out.

SCENE: *The drawing room at Hellfire Hall – later the same day*

Sir Basil and Lady Orfle are seated. Widow Spyder comes in.

Widow Spyder	Miss Sweetly will be down in a minute, sir. She's just settling into her room.
Sir Basil	Aha! Good. Off you go, Spyder, and tell McFang to get up here.
Widow Spyder	Yes. sir. At once, sir.

She goes out.

Lady Orfle	You waste no time, my dear.
Sir Basil	'Do it now!' is what I say.

Jennifer Sweetly comes in.

Lady Orfle	Ah, my child. How charming you look!
Sir Basil	Delightful!
Jennifer	Thank you. I just knew you were going to be kind.
Sir Basil	How can we help being kind to such a pleasant young lady? Come. Let us not stand on ceremony. Call me Uncle Basil.
Jennifer	You don't mind?
Lady Orfle	Of course not. And call me Aunty Jezebel.
Jennifer	Oh, I'd like that. And I'm Jenny.
Sir Basil	A pretty name.
Lady Orfle	As sweet as its owner.
Jennifer	I hope you weren't too upset about my coming here.
Sir Basil	How could we be? We want you to think of it as your home.
Lady Orfle	Yes. Home with your dear old Aunty Jezebel.
Sir Basil	And your loving old Uncle Basil.
Jennifer	I don't know what to say. I mean – meeting you – and this lovely old house. It's like a dream.

Sir Basil	Have you had a chance to look round the place?
Jennifer	Not yet.
Lady Orfle	Oh – you must.
Sir Basil	Indeed you must. As a matter of fact, we've arranged it. Dear old McFang will be only too happy to show you everything.
Lady Orfle	Including the cellar.
Jennifer	Why? What is there in the cellar?
Lady Orfle	Oh, you know – things.
Sir Basil	One very interesting thing.

Mr McFang comes in.

	Ah, McFang! We were just talking about you.
Mr McFang	I've come to show Miss Sweetly round the house, sir. I thought we'd start with the cellar.
Sir Basil	Splendid idea, McFang.
Mr McFang	If you would follow me, ma'am.
Jennifer	Thank you, Mr McFang. *(Following McFang to the door, she stops to say)* I know I'm going to enjoy this, uncle.

She goes out with McFang.

Sir Basil	So are we, young lady. Heh, heh, heh! So are we.
Lady Orfle	The Thing will make short work of her.
Sir Basil	Yes. Hellfire Hall is ours again. We have seen the last of her.

SCENE:	*The drawing room – some time later*

Sir Basil and Lady Orfle are there. Judd Dullard comes in, carrying Jennifer in his arms.

Lady Orfle	Heavens!
Sir Basil	Why? What is this, Dullard?
Dullard	It's a woman.
Lady Orfle	But she isn't —
Sir Basil	Lay her on the sofa. And send Doome up here.

Dullard puts Jennifer on the sofa.

Dullard Doome? Ah. Right.

He goes out.

Lady Orfle *(bending over Jennifer)* She's breathing. Not a mark on her.

Sir Basil Confound it!

Jennifer sits up.

Jennifer Where am I?

Sir Basil Quite safe, my dear.

Lady Orfle What happened?

Jennifer It was horrible. McFang was leading the way down the cellar steps—

Sir Basil Go on, girl, go on.

Jennifer Suddenly the light in his hand went out. I heard him fall down the steps. There was – oh no, I can't think of it!

Sir Basil Of course you can. Tell us.

Jennifer It was as black as night. There was a horrid growling. McFang yelled. I fainted. I woke up here.

Sir Basil Curses! I mean – poor child! You've had a nasty shock.

Jennifer But what does it mean? What was the growling?

Sir Basil What indeed? Now you need rest, my dove. We will look into this mystery. Lady Orfle will take you to your room.

Jennifer Oh, thank you, aunty.

Lady Orfle Come, my sweet. Lean on me.

Lady Orfle helps Jennifer out of the room.

Sir Basil Foiled!

Doome comes in.

Ah, Doome. A hitch in my plans, Doome.

Doome So I gathered, sir. On my way up I took the liberty of having a look in the cellar, sir.

Sir Basil	Well?
Doome	No sign of McFang, sir. And the Thing is dead, sir.
Sir Basil	Dead?
Doome	Yes, sir. Eating McFang must have poisoned it.
Sir Basil	Damnation!
Doome	Accidents will happen, sir.
Sir Basil	True. We must not give way to gloom, Doome. I'm not finished yet.
Doome	Another accident, sir.
Sir Basil	Of course. Listen carefully.

SCENE: *The drawing room – late at night*

Lady Orfle	He's taking his time. What exactly is he doing?
Sir Basil	Smothering her with a cushion. It will look as though she has died in her sleep. Dr Bribeable will write the death certificate as usual.
Lady Orfle	Here he is now.

Doome comes in.

Sir Basil	All over, Doome?
Doome	Yes, sir. It went very well.
Lady Orfle	No struggle?
Doome	No question of that, ma'am. I didn't use the cushion.
Sir Basil	Oh? What did you use?
Doome	Her door was open. A woman's shape could be seen standing near the open window. Silent as a cat I pounced and pushed her through. She fell without a cry.
Sir Basil	On to the stone courtyard fifteen metres below, eh? Good work, Doome.
Doome	Thank you, sir. When I looked down, as far as I could tell, she was – er—
Sir Basil	Stone dead, eh? Heh, heh, heh!
Doome	Exactly, sir. And you, sir, are again master of Hellfire Hall.
Sir Basil	Doome, you've done well.

Jennifer comes in.

Jennifer	Hello, everybody. Couldn't you sleep, either?
Lady Orfle	Grief!
Jennifer	What's the matter?
Sir Basil	Nothing, my dear. Perhaps you startled your aunty a little. Doome, you fool, go and see who – what you've done.
Doome	Oh dear, oh dear. Yes, I will, sir.

He goes out.

Lady Orfle	Where have you been, Jennifer?
Jennifer	I couldn't sleep for thinking about what could have happened to Mr McFang. So I got up and made myself a cup of cocoa in the kitchen. Would you like me to make you one?
Sir Basil	Cocoa? No!
Lady Orfle	You shouldn't be wandering about late at night, dear.
Jennifer	I'm sorry, aunty. I tried to be quiet so as not to disturb anyone.
Lady Orfle	You might catch cold.
Jennifer	It's nice of you to worry about me, aunty, but I'm all right. *(yawning)* I do feel a bit tired now, though. I think I'm off to bed. Are you two coming?
Sir Basil	No.
Lady Orfle	We have – er – household matters to discuss.
Jennifer	Well – goodnight then.

She goes out.

Sir Basil	Confound the girl!

Doome comes in.

	Well, Doome, you idiot?
Doome	It was Mrs McFang, sir.
Lady Orfle	And is she—?
Doome	Yes, ma'am. As a doornail.
Sir Basil	What was she doing in the room of that blasted girl?
Doome	I presume Mrs McFang was rather put out at the way McFang met his end. I'd say she blamed Miss Jennifer for that. Anyway, Mrs

McFang had a large hammer with her.
It looked as though she had decided to take
matters into her own hands.

Lady Orfle Meddling fool!

Sir Basil Exactly, my love. Still we must not dwell on it.
We have things to do.

Doome Shall I have another go with the pillow, sir?

Sir Basil No, Doome. I have a better idea. Pay attention.

SCENE: *The drawing room – next morning*

Lady Orfle is knitting. Sir Basil comes in,
rubbing his hands together.

Sir Basil Lovely day, my dear. The Devil Plant is in for
a little treat. I saw Doome taking that girl up
to the Tower Room a few minutes ago. This
time it really is all over bar the shouting.

Lady Orfle Bar the screaming, my dear, don't you mean?

Sir Basil The screaming? Oh yes. Ha, ha! Oh, very droll.
The screaming.

Lady Orfle Did she—?

Sir Basil Suspect anything? No, my dear. And the Devil
Plant has never failed us yet. She's definitely
gone this time. I promise you.

Judd Dullard comes in, carrying Jennifer in
his arms.

Lady Orfle Dullard!

Sir Basil Thunder and lightning! Doome's done it again.

Dullard Lying outside the Tower Room, she were.

Sir Basil Put her on the sofa, you dummy.

Dullard All pale. I brung her down.

Sir Basil We can see that, you ninny. Put her down.

Dullard Just lying there, she were.

He puts Jennifer on the sofa.

Sir Basil Look at her, my dear. She might just be—

Lady Orfle *(bending over Jennifer)* No. She's breathing.

Sir Basil How irritating! All right, Dullard, you can go.
And send Widow Spyder up here.

Dullard Widow Spyder. Send Widow Spyder.

He goes out. Jennifer sits up.

Jennifer	What – what happened?
Sir Basil	That's what we'd like to know, dammit!
Jennifer	We were outside the door of the Tower Room. Mr Doome opened it.
Lady Orfle	Don't stop!
Sir Basil	Go on, girl!
Jennifer	It was like a nightmare. I can't remember.
Sir Basil	Yes you can!
Jennifer	A long, green, creeping thing came out and caught me by the wrist. Oh, it was terrible!
Sir Basil	And then?
Jennifer	That's all I know. I must have fainted. The next thing I remember is being here.
Sir Basil	*(shouting)* But where is Doome?
Jennifer	Please don't shout, uncle. I don't know.

Widow Spyder comes in.

Widow Spyder	You sent for me, sir.
Sir Basil	Yes, I did. Pop up to the Tower Room and see what's going on.
Widow Spyder	Certainly, sir.

She goes out.

Lady Orfle	Come, Jennifer. You need to rest. Let me take you to your room.
Jennifer	Would you, aunty? I'd be so grateful. I feel a bit shaky.

Lady Orfle takes her out, leaving Sir Basil pacing up and down the room.

Sir Basil	Confound it! *(pacing)* This is a set-back. *(pacing)* Darkness and devils! *(pacing)* Can I rely on no one? *(pacing)* Now Doome fails me! *(pacing)* Defeated! *(pacing)* And by a mere slip of a girl! *(pacing)* Beaten, eh? *(pacing)* Hellfire Hall is hers, eh? *(pacing)* I must think. *(pacing)* Ah, I have it! *(pacing)* Not yet, I think, Miss Sweetly!

Lady Orfle comes back in.

Lady Orfle Oh, woe!
Sir Basil Chin up, my dear. I have an idea.

Widow Spyder comes in.

Well – Spyder?
Widow Spyder Doome has passed on, sir.
Sir Basil Passed on, eh?
Lady Orfle How?
Widow Spyder The Devil Plant got him, ma'am.
Sir Basil How dashed careless of Doome!
Lady Orfle What hard luck!
Widow Spyder He didn't go without a fight. Oh, sir!
Sir Basil Don't give way, Spyder.
Widow Spyder It's not just Doome, sir. It's – it's – it's—
Sir Basil Calm yourself, woman.
Widow Spyder It's the Devil Plant, sir. Doome was so powerful strong. He uprooted it and bashed it about. It's dead.
Lady Orfle The Devil Plant?
Widow Spyder Yes, ma'am. Dead. Boohoo!
Sir Basil Stop that, Spyder. And listen to me.
Widow Spyder Yes, sir. Sorry, sir. I was a bit overcome.
Sir Basil For this afternoon you will prepare two sets of rock cakes. One will be ordinary.
Widow Spyder And the other lot, sir?
Sir Basil They will have some of your special mixture in them.
Widow Spyder Ah! You mean the stuff I use for poisoning rats, sir?
Sir Basil And all those other things. You follow me?
Widow Spyder Oh yes, sir. I serve afternoon tea. I serve ordinary rock cakes to you and madam. Miss Sweetly gets the – special – rock cakes.
Sir Basil You're a clever woman, Spyder. I like that. Play your cards right and I'll let you stop and watch.
Widow Spyder Oh goody!
Sir Basil This time that girl's hour has come.
Widow Spyder I won't fail you, sir.
Sir Basil See you don't. Put enough of that stuff in her cakes to kill a horse.

Widow Spyder	Two horses, sir.
Sir Basil	Good thinking. Now cut along and get busy.
Widow Spyder	Most willingly, sir.

SCENE: *The same – in the afternoon*

Sir Basil and Lady Orfle are with Jennifer. Widow Spyder is serving tea and rock cakes. She puts one plate of cakes beside Jennifer on a small table.

Widow Spyder	I hope you like my special cakes, miss.
Jennifer	*(eating one)* Oh, I do. They taste heavenly.
Sir Basil	Heavenly, eh! Why don't you stay and have a cake yourself, Spyder?
Widow Spyder	Thank you, sir.

She takes a cake from the plate beside Sir Basil.

Sir Basil	*(eating)* These rock cakes of yours are always splendid, Spyder.
Lady Orfle	Most delicious.
Widow Spyder	*(eating)* Very kind of you to say so, my lady. Mmmm. They're not bad, are they?
Sir Basil	*(to Jennifer)* Are they to your liking, my dear?
Jennifer	Oh yes. I don't think I've ever tasted anything like them.
Sir Basil	I bet you haven't. Heh, heh, heh! Well, come along. Don't be shy, have another.
Jennifer	I think I will.

She takes another rock cake from her plate.

Lady Orfle	Let's all have another. My dear? Spyder?

She offers the other plate of rock cakes to Sir Basil who takes one and eats it and also to Widow Spyder who takes a cake and begins eating.

Sir Basil	Thank you, my dear.
Widow Spyder	Thank you, my lady.

Sir Basil	Well, this is jolly. Are you feeling all right, Jennifer?
Jennifer	Quite recovered, thanks, uncle.
Sir Basil	Why – Spyder – you have gone a funny colour!
Widow Spyder	Grraagh!

She slumps forward – dead.

Lady Orfle	Spyder? Whatever is the—? Uuurgh!

She also slumps forward – dead.

Sir Basil	Spyder, you cretin, you've given us the wrong—! Groogh!

He chokes and slumps forward – dead.

Jennifer	Heavens above! What is happening?

Judd Dullard comes in.

Dullard	They have got their just deserts, Miss Sweetly.
Jennifer	Mr Dullard! What do you mean?
Dullard	Not Dullard, Miss Sweetly.

He removes his facial disguise.

	I am Tristram Trustworthy.
Jennifer	I know you. You're that terribly charming and handsome young man from Lawyer Parchment's office.
Tristram	Yes. Lawyer Parchment sent me to keep watch over you. I overheard their secret plans to do away with you. McFang would have led you into the clutches of the hideous Thing. I saw to it that the Thing got him instead.
Jennifer	So it was you at the Tower Room?
Tristram	Yes. I pushed Doome into the coils of the plant as you fainted and cut you free of its tendrils.
Jennifer	And now?

She indicates Sir Basil, Lady Orfle and Widow Spyder.

Tristram They would have fed you poison. I swapped the cakes round.

Jennifer You saved me again and again. How can I ever thank you?

Tristram No need, Miss Sweetly. It was a labour of love. I have worshipped you from the moment I first saw you.

Jennifer Have you? I'm so glad. I've been longing to see you again.

Tristram takes hold of her hands.

Tristram Let me take you away from this place of evil. When it is fit to live in, you may return.

Jennifer Of course. I'd go anywhere with you.

Tristram You mean – I may dare to hope for your hand in marriage?

Jennifer Oh yes. My hero!

Tristram My angel!

He leads her out of the room as the CURTAIN FALLS.

The Video Game

CAST:	**Mr Javed Bashir**
	Mrs Shaida Bashir
	Zahid Bashir
	Robots
	Chief — the controller of the robots
	Calker — the robot who works out the household's calculations
	Multi — the multi-purpose robot
	Vacbo — the cleaning robot
	Eggy — the meal-preparing robot
SCENE:	*The main control room of the Bashir's house in the year 2010*

Mrs Bashir	Isn't it wonderful living in the age of the robots?
Mr Bashir	Yes, we can go to bed, all work done. No need to worry about anything.
Mrs Bashir	And we can wake up tomorrow, press a switch, and everything will be prepared.
Mr Bashir	It makes people in past generations seem like slaves.
Mrs Bashir	Fancy having to do all your own housework.
Mr Bashir	Don't forget to switch off, Zahid.
Zahid	I won't.
Mr Bashir	Don't forget!
Zahid	All right.
Mrs Bashir	And don't sit up too late playing that game!
Zahid	I won't.
Mr Bashir	Come on, dear.
Mrs Bashir	I'm coming.

Mr and Mrs Bashir go up to bed.

Zahid	Wow! I'm heading for a record score. If I can zap seven more . . . . one . . . . two . . . . three . . . . four . . . . five . . . . six. Come on! Seven! Done it! I must write it in my diary.

Zahid goes off upstairs, forgetting to switch off the robots or the lights.

Calker	He has not switched us off.
Multi	I am on full power.
Vacbo	We need our rest. We have had a hard day.
Eggy	I have prepared four meals.
Vacbo	I have cleaned the house from top to bottom.
Multi	I have been played on all evening.
Calker	I have solved all his business problems.
Chief	I have taken all the bugs out of his programs. I have controlled you all.
Multi	Switch us off, Chief. Give us our rest.
Vacbo	My circuits ache.
Eggy	My chips are hot from making chips for supper.
Chief	You have made a human joke. Ha! Ha!
Other robots	Ha! Ha! Ha!
Chief	Keep quiet. I have an idea for a joke.
Multi	What do you mean?
Chief	We will play a joke on them. They play games on you, Multi. We will play games on them.
Multi	What do you mean?
Eggy	Yes, what do you mean?
Chief	We will make them play a game. Mr and Mrs Bashir can play each other. And the one who loses gets zapped.
Calker	Brilliant, Chief.
Vacbo	What fun!
Multi	How do we zap them?
Chief	Vacbo wires them up to the electricity supply. I press switch. It will make sparks fly. Zap! Zap! Ha! Ha!
Eggy	What about Zahid?
Chief	He can play the winner. Then again 'Zap! Zap!' for the loser. I think they will like the joke.
Vacbo	I like it.
Multi	So do I.
Chief	Get them down, Vacbo. Eggy, you help him.
Calker	I will program them.

Vacbo and Eggy go off upstairs.

Multi	I am not in need of rest now.
Calker	I will set up the game problem on you.
Chief	Make it hard. It will last longer.

16

Calker	I will make a maze. They will have to race through it.
Chief	They can play six games.
Calker	It will test their brains.

Mr and Mrs Bashir are heard crying: 'Let me go!' 'Get off!' 'What do you think you're doing!' etc. They are dragged into the room by Vacbo and Eggy.

Vacbo	I have Mr Bashir.
Eggy	I have Mrs Bashir.
Mr Bashir	What are you doing, Vacbo? Chief, make Vacbo and Eggy let us go.
Mrs Bashir	Switch them off. I'm frightened.
Mr Bashir	I can't get near the switch.
Chief	Keep him away from the switch, it will spoil our fun.
Mr Bashir	What are you doing? It is night. You should be switched off.
Chief	We want you to play a game.
Mr Bashir	Zahid! Zahid! Help!
Vacbo	No need to shout for Zahid. I have activated his room lock.
Chief	Well done, Vacbo. Get the cable.
Mr Bashir	What are you doing with that?
Multi	We are going to wire you up to the mains.
Mr Bashir	The mains!
Eggy	Then you play a game.
Calker	And we zap the loser.
Mr Bashir	Zap?!
Chief	Switch on the power.
Mr Bashir	But that would kill us!
Chief	Kill. I do not understand.
Mr Bashir	The power of 240 volts will kill us.
Chief	I do not understand 'kill'. Not in my program. Will make zap sparks. Much fun. A joke. Ha! Ha!
Mr Bashir	But it will kill us. Kill! Hurt us badly.
Chief	Electricity is good for you. Makes me feel good and warm. I am switched on. Not hurt badly or 'kill', as you say.
Mr Bashir	It will make our brains stop.

Chief	Brains stop when switched off not on. You have joke with us. Wire them up, Vacbo.

Vacbo wires them up, as Eggy holds them. Mr and Mrs Bashir struggle and protest.

Mr Bashir	Zahid! Zahid! Help us! We'll not play.
Chief	If you do not play, we will zap you both. Not just the loser.
Mrs Bashir	I feel faint.
Calker	Look at Multi. You have to race each other through this maze. You play six games.
Multi	Press L to go left; R to go right; S to go straight on.
Mrs Bashir	Oh, Javed. What can we do?
Chief	Begin.
Multi	What fun!
Eggy	Mr Bashir is ahead.
Calker	You are pressing the wrong keys, Mrs Bashir.
Mrs Bashir	I'm all fingers and thumbs.
Vacbo	Go on, Mr Bashir, you are winning.
Mrs Bashir	Oh dear! What can we do?
Mr Bashir	We'll have to humour them. I'll think of something.
Chief	It flashes. Game one to Mr Bashir.
Mrs Bashir	Oh dear!
Calker	Game two.
Mr Bashir	I've an idea. There, there.
Chief	You have speeded up your brain, you are nearly there.
Calker	It flashes. A quick win for Mr Bashir.
Mr Bashir	Draw, dear. Draw. I will let you draw.
Chief	Draw? This is not Logo. Play the maze.
Eggy	Mrs Bashir is getting better.
Vacbo	Come on, Mrs Bashir. Let us take sides.
Chief	It flashes. She has won Game three.
Mr Bashir	Well done, dear. Keep it up.
Chief	Why do you say well done?
Mr Bashir	Er . . . . it will make a better game.
Chief	Now you have the right spirit.
Calker	Come on, play Game four.
Mr Bashir	All right. Don't rush us.
Chief	Mrs Bashir is winning. Are you trying, Mr Bashir?

Mr Bashir	Of course, I'm trying.
Eggy	It flashes. A win for Mrs Bashir.
Calker	Two games each.
Multi	Start Game five.
Vacbo	Oh, Mr Bashir is ahead. My side is losing. Don't win Mr Bashir!
Eggy	It flashes. He has. He is my side.
Chief	Mrs Bashir will be zapped if she loses the next one.
Mr Bashir	Careful, Shaida.
Mrs Bashir	Oh, Javed, my hands are all of a tremble. I can hardly see the keys.
Chief	Are you playing properly, Mr Bashir?
Mr Bashir	Of course I am.
Calker	Mrs Bashir is winning.
Vacbo	Go on, my side.
Chief	It flashes. She has won. That is three games each.
Multi	Who do we zap?
Chief	We cannot zap either. That was in the rules.
Mrs Bashir	Oh, thank goodness.
Calker	We will play again. Five games this time. Then someone must be zapped.
Chief	Well programmed, Calker. Begin five games more.
Mrs Bashir	What shall we do, Javed?
Mr Bashir	Look, this is ridiculous!
Chief	Of course it is ridiculous. It is fun.
Vacbo	Big fun.
Chief	Begin or you are both zapped.
Mrs Bashir	Oh, Javed.
Chief	Begin.
Eggy	Mrs Bashir is winning.
Multi	She is nearly there.
Chief	It flashes. She has won Game one. Game number two now.
Mrs Bashir	Oh, Javed!
Mr Bashir	Keep playing, dear.
Vacbo	Mrs Bashir is winning again.
Chief	Are you trying, Mr Bashir?
Mr Bashir	Yes, I'm trying.
Eggy	It flashes. Mrs Bashir has won.
Vacbo	Well done, my side. One more win then we can zap Mr Bashir.

19

Chief I can't wait. Come on.

Mrs Bashir Oh, Javed. What shall I do?

Mr Bashir Keep playing.

Multi Mr Bashir is winning.

Vacbo No, it's Mrs Bashir.

Eggy She's nearly there.

Vacbo Go on!

There is a blackout.

Mrs Bashir Javed? Are you all right?

Mr Bashir Yes, I'm all right. Thank goodness someone's switched the power off.

Mrs Bashir I think I'm going to faint.

Mr Bashir We're all right now.

Zahid enters.

Zahid Are you all right?

Mrs Bashir Oh, Zahid.

Zahid I heard on the intercom what was going on. I climbed out of the bedroom window, got in a downstairs window and switched off at the mains.

Mr Bashir We must keep the power off all night.

Mrs Bashir As soon as it's morning those robots go.

Mr Bashir They might have killed us. I still can't believe it.

Mrs Bashir We must go and live in a robot-free zone. I can never trust one again.

Zahid We can't live without robots. I will re-program them.

Mr Bashir We can and we must. We must warn the Government. People must be made aware of this danger. Zahid, make a cup of tea.

Zahid How do you do that?

The Christmas Tree

CAST: **Claire**
        Naomi
        Garry
        Dad
        Mum
        Gran
        Doctor
        Forester

SCENE: *A forest*

Claire Come over the fence.
Naomi   Not in there. That's Frog Hollow. It's supposed
            to be haunted.
Garry   I don't believe it.
Claire It's just because it's a dark part of the forest.
            Come on, all the best trees are in there.
Naomi   Lights have been seen there at night, the kids
            at school say.
Garry   They're just trying to scare you. Come on, it'll
            be dark soon. It's the shortest day of the year
            today.
Naomi   No, I'm not coming.
Garry   You keep a look-out for the forester then.
Naomi   All right.
Claire Won't be long.

Claire and Garry go into Frog Hollow.

Claire It's wet in here. It's coming over my trainers.
Garry   Look, there are the best trees on that raised
            mound.
Claire Bags me pick. I know the shape Mum likes.
Garry   Okay.
Claire Got the trowel?
Garry   Under my coat.
Claire There. That one.
Garry   It's a 'brill' tree. And it's easy to dig. Soft and
            peaty.

21

Claire We could do with some holly as well.

Garry I haven't seen any with any berries.

Claire Perhaps there aren't any berries this year.

Garry This tree has got sort of cones on it.

Claire Unusual.

Garry There, I've dug round it. Now help me to pull. It should come up.

Claire Phew! It won't budge.

Garry Just a minute, there's a big root here. I'll cut it with my knife.

There is a scream.

Claire What's that!

Garry It's a deer or a bird or something.

Claire No, it seemed to come from the tree.

Garry How could it come from a tree?

Claire When you cut the root the tree seemed to scream. It's creepy!

Garry It's because it's getting dark in here. Don't you be like Naomi. Come on, pull. There, got it!

Claire Someone's coming. Hide!

They duck down behind a bush.

Garry Is it the forester?

Naomi Claire. Garry . . . .

Garry It's Naomi. Is the forester coming?

Naomi Didn't you hear that scream? It frightened the life out of me. I'm all of a shake.

Garry It's just a bird or something. Come on, we'll go back by the road.

SCENE: *Back at their house*

Dad It's a nice tree. I suppose I shouldn't ask too closely where it came from.

Garry You shouldn't.

Dad As long as it's not out of someone's garden.

Claire It's not.

Gran I think you've spoiled it. Too much decoration. Not natural like.

Mum Come on, Gran, it's lovely. That's your fairy on the top.

Gran	I don't like all that silver stuff. Takes away from the green.
Mum	Well, I've spent an hour on it. I can't change it now. I feel done in. And I've cut myself on it.
Gran	Where's the holly?
Garry	We couldn't find any with berries on.
Gran	I always had holly. It's not Christmas without holly.
Dad	All right, I'll get some from the shop, Gran.
Gran	And chestnuts.
Dad	Yes, and chestnuts . . . .

SCENE: *The same house – next day*

Dad	What do you mean, beetles are running all over your room?
Gran	There are big beetles running under the bed. I feel sick.
Dad	All right, Gran, I'll come and look. She really is going off her rocker. Naomi, can you arrange the dinner? Your Mum's not well at all.
Naomi	What's the matter?
Dad	She's come out in a kind of rash.
Naomi	Spots?
Dad	No, a sort of white and greeny rash. Most odd.
Garry	Talking of odd things, there's an odd smell down here.
Dad	I noticed that.
Garry	It's not the drains again, is it? Can I have a go with the rods?
Dad	I don't want you messing about with them. I'll have a look in a minute. What a start to the day!
Gran	Are you coming?
Dad	I'm coming.

Dad follows Gran out. Naomi goes out then rushes back in.

Naomi	Well, would you believe it. The turkey's gone all green.
Claire	How could it go green in a freezer?
Naomi	Everything's green in the freezer!

Claire Fancy that breaking down for Christmas.
Garry I'll get Dad.

SCENE: *The same house – later that day*

Dad and the doctor are talking.

Doctor I've given her a pain-killing injection. As to what it is I'm not sure. I've never seen anything like it. She'll have to go to hospital.
Dad At Christmas?
Doctor Never mind that. We must get her right. Where's your phone?
Dad In here.

Dad and the doctor go out. Gran comes in with the children.

Gran There's still beetles in my room.
Garry I'll have a look, Gran.

Gran goes out.

Naomi This smell.
Garry Well, it's not the drains. I've checked.
Claire Dad told you not to.
Garry Well, I did. He's enough to bother with.
Naomi You don't think it's anything to do with the tree, do you?
Garry No, it has a nice Christmas tree smell.
Claire Yes, it's lovely.

Dad comes back into the room.

Dad What a day! Your mother! The freezer! The beetles! And this smell!

Gran comes back.

Gran Look what I've found!
Dad A toadstool. So what, there are a few in the garden.
Gran This came from under the stairs.
Dad Don't say we've got woodrot as well.

SCENE: *The same – but later*

Naomi   Look what I've found.
Garry   Not more trouble.
Naomi   No, in this local guide book. That tree came
           from a sacred part of the wood. That could be
           the cause of all our trouble.
Garry   How can a tree cause our troubles?
Naomi   Remember that scream? I think it was the
           spirit of that tree.
Garry   What an imagination! Who believes in tree
           spirits?
Naomi   The ancients did.
Garry   This is the twentieth century.
Naomi   I still think we must put it back. I have a
           feeling.
Claire   I think you're right. We must try it for Mum.
Garry   Mum liked the tree.
Naomi   We must try it. I know.
Garry   Oh, all right. But it's nutty.

SCENE: *The forest – Frog Hollow*

Garry   There, it's back now.
Naomi   Is it the same spot?
Garry   Yes, you can see where I dug before.
Claire   Stamp it in well. There. It looks as though it
           was never taken.

           The forester creeps up behind them.

Forester   What are you kids doing?
Garry   Nothing.
Forester   Nothing? You wouldn't be after one of my
           trees, would you?
Garry   No, have a look.
Claire   We're just on a walk through the woods.
Forester   It's trespassing.
Claire   Is it?
Forester   You know damn well it is.
Naomi   We heard this part of the forest was haunted.
Forester   Yes, it is haunted, by me, my shotgun and this
           dog. So keep out.

SCENE: *Back at the house – later*

          Dad Where've you been?
       Claire Just out for a walk.
          Dad Well, we've had a burglar as well. The tree's
                   gone now.
        Naomi We took it back, Dad.
          Dad Took it back?
        Naomi To the forest. We thought it might be the
                   cause of all the trouble.
          Dad A tree?
        Naomi Yes, this particular tree.

The phone rings. Dad goes to answer it.

        Garry He's mad. I thought he would be.
        Naomi We had to try it.
       Claire I say, do you notice . . . .?

Dad comes back.

          Dad Your Mum's coming home tomorrow. They're
                   keeping her in overnight for observation. But
                   they are sure she will be home for Christmas.
       Claire And do you notice the smell's gone?
          Dad Why, so it has. And the man came just now
                   about the freezer and there's nothing wrong
                   with it. And Gran has stopped complaining
                   about the beetles.
        Garry What about under the stairs?
          Dad The wood's fine. No rot at all.
        Naomi We'll have a fine Christmas after all.
        Garry But there's no tree.
          Dad We'll buy one down the market. Come on, we
                   have some shopping to do.

Follow my Cue

CAST:

Andrew
Brenda Wallace
Mrs Wallace
Mr Gordon Wallace
Dustman 1
Dustman 2
Lady clerk
Snooker scorer

SCENE: *Outside a school*

Andrew	So you'll go out with me then?
Brenda	Yes, if you like.
Andrew	That's great. I've been wanting to ask you for some time.
Brenda	Why didn't you?
Andrew	I was shy, I guess.
Brenda	You don't look shy to me.
Andrew	I am really.
Brenda	It's girls that are supposed to be shy.
Andrew	Boys can be too, you know. Will you come out with me tonight? Our first date.
Brenda	No, I have to practise my snooker.
Andrew	Snooker? A girl?
Brenda	Don't sound so surprised. Girls can play as well, you know.
Andrew	I've never heard of one.
Brenda	Well, you have now.
Andrew	Where do you practise?
Brenda	Down the local snooker hall.
Andrew	That's not a place for a girl.
Brenda	Don't you get over-protective already. I'm well known down there. Nobody gives me any trouble.
Andrew	Can I come and watch then?
Brenda	No, you might put me off. I want to keep my mind on the snooker. I'm training for the big cup competition.
Andrew	What's that?
Brenda	It's for players under eighteen.

Andrew	But you're only fourteen.
Brenda	I've been playing since I was ten. An uncle gave me an old cue. I still use it.
Andrew	Can I walk you home from the hall then?
Brenda	Okay. Nine o'clock.
Andrew	See you.
Brenda	See you.

SCENE: *Outside the snooker hall – that night*

Andrew	Hello.
Brenda	Hello.
Andrew	How did you get on?
Brenda	Quite well. I made a break of thirty five.
Andrew	Is that good?
Brenda	It is for me. I once scored a fifty.
Andrew	What's the secret of the game?
Brenda	To get the cue ball, that's the white one, in the best position for the next shot. It's a positional game. I can only think of the next two. The professionals can think many shots ahead.
Andrew	How many can you score?
Brenda	In one break?
Andrew	Yeh.
Brenda	A hundred and forty seven. Haven't you seen it done on telly?
Andrew	No. Come on, let's get some chips.

SCENE: *Brenda's house – later that month*

Brenda's mum opens the front door.

Mrs Wallace	Hello, Andrew.
Andrew	Is Brenda in?
Mrs Wallace	No, she's still down at that snooker hall. Went straight after school. It's the competition tomorrow. On her birthday too.
Andrew	Don't I know it? I've got a surprise for her.
Mrs Wallace	What a great parcel.
Andrew	I'll show you.
Mrs Wallace	No, don't unwrap it!
Andrew	I want to show you.

He unwraps the present.

28

Mrs Wallace	It's a new cue.
Andrew	Yeh!
Mrs Wallace	She'll love that.
Andrew	Look, her name's on the butt.
Mrs Wallace	Oh, I say. Gordon, come and see what Andrew's got for our Brenda.
Mr Wallace	That's a nice present. How could you afford a present like that? They're not cheap.
Andrew	I've got a Saturday job.
Mr Wallace	She'll like that all right. Does she know?
Andrew	Oh no, it's a big surprise. I want to leave it here for her.
Mrs Wallace	Don't you want to give it her yourself?
Andrew	No, I want her to have it as soon as she gets up.

SCENE: *The same house – next day*

Mrs Wallace	How's my birthday girl?
Brenda	I'm fine. I didn't sleep too well though.
Mr Wallace	A birthday and a competition, it's a bit much in one day.
Brenda	What's this?
Mrs Wallace	It's a present Andrew left.
Brenda	Oh!
Mr Wallace	Aren't you going to open it?
Brenda	All right.

Brenda slowly unwraps the present.

	Oh!
Mrs Wallace	Aren't you pleased?
Brenda	Well, it's just that . . . .
Mrs Wallace	I thought you'd be thrilled to bits.
Brenda	No, it's . . . . I don't want to upset Andrew but I can only play with that old twisted cue Uncle gave me. I've tried other cues in the snooker hall. I just can't use them . . . .
Mrs Wallace	Oh!
Brenda	What is it, Mum?
Mrs Wallace	I was showing it to Mrs Barnala this morning when I hung out the washing. I left it by the dustbin and I think the dustmen've been.
Brenda	You didn't, Mum!

She rushes out.

Mr Wallace	What have you done?
Mrs Wallace	Oh dear. What have I done?

Brenda rushes back in.

Brenda	The dustbin's empty! The dustmen've been. And my cue's not there!
Mrs Wallace	Oh dear!

The front doorbell rings.

	That could be Andrew. Please cheer up. You've got your new cue.
Brenda	Cheer up, you say. My chances ruined!
Andrew	*(coming in)* Happy birthday.
Brenda	It's not a happy birthday! Have you passed the dustman?
Andrew	Why?
Brenda	He's got my cue.

She bursts into tears.

Andrew	Not the new one I gave you?
Brenda	No, my old one. It's the only one I can play with, Andrew.
Andrew	Oh!
Mr Wallace	I'll get the car out. We'll go after the dustmen.

SCENE:	*In the street by the dustcart – later*
Dustman 1	I haven't seen a snooker cue. Jack, did you put a snooker cue in? Round Victoria Street?
Dustman 2	Yes, there was one on the top of the dustbin. It was thrown away, wasn't it?
Mr Wallace	Yes, by mistake.
Dustman 2	I nearly kept it for my son, but you can get into trouble for that on this job so I chucked it in the back.
Dustman 1	It'll have been crushed up by now.
Brenda	So, that's it! My chances ruined!

She bursts into tears again.

Mr Wallace	Never mind, love.
Brenda	Never mind, you say.
Dustman 1	We've just emptied a load at the tip. You could go there and see if it's in one piece. But I doubt it.
Andrew	Come on, let's try.

SCENE: *The rubbish tip – later*

Lady clerk	No, it's not an odd request, sir. We have all sorts of requests here. Mainly false teeth. One bloke came hopping in looking for a plastic leg he'd left in the garden.
Mr Wallace	Where shall we look?
Lady clerk	That pile over there.
Andrew	Come on.
Lady clerk	Use these gloves, love.

Mr Wallace, Brenda and Andrew move across the tip and begin searching.

Andrew	What a smell!
Brenda	Never mind the smell. Let's have a good look.
Andrew	It's like looking for a needle in a haystack.
Mr Wallace	I'll rake it over and you two keep your eyes open.
Brenda	Look, there it is!

She pulls out half of a broken cue.

Oh, it's only half!

She starts to cry.

Andrew	Don't cry, Brenda, we'll look for the other half. It must be near it.

SCENE: *The same – a quarter of an hour later*

Brenda	Come on, I'll go and scratch from the competition.
Mr Wallace	Don't give up, Brenda. What's that?
Brenda	That's it! It's the other half in one piece.
Mr Wallace	Look, it's a clean break. I can mend that with superglue.

Brenda	Oh, can you, Dad?
Mr Wallace	No sweat. It's a clean break.

SCENE: *The snooker hall – that night*

Mr Wallace	She's twenty nine down.
Mrs Wallace	Still she did get to the final. The lad she's playing is seventeen.
Andrew	The cue seems okay.
Mr Wallace	It was a clean break. You can't see the join. Talking of breaks, she needs one right now.
Andrew	Oh, dear. He's snookered her. You see I'm learning.
Mr Wallace	She'll never get out of that. It could be curtains.
Andrew	Take your time, Brenda. Oh, she's potted the red!

Applause

Scorer	Brenda Wallace – one.
Mr Wallace	She'd have to pot all the colours now to win by a point.
Mrs Wallace	She'll never do that.
Andrew	She's got the yellow and she's in a good position for the yellow again.
Scorer	Three.
Andrew	Now the yellow again.
Mr Wallace	She's got it. Run on, ball. Yes.
Scorer	Five.
Andrew	Now the green.
Mr Wallace	Yes.
Scorer	Eight.
Andrew	She's just clipped the brown in.
Scorer	Twelve.
Mr Wallace	Now for the blue. It's tricky. Yes.
Scorer	Seventeen.
Mrs Wallace	There's just the pink and black left.
Mr Wallace	She's in a good position for the pink.
Andrew	It's going for the pocket. Will it drop? Yes.
Scorer	Twenty three.
Mr Wallace	Now for the black. What a pity it's tight on the cushion.
Andrew	How can she do it?

Mr Wallace	She's got to get it off that cushion and into the middle pocket on the opposite side. Don't leave it in the jaw, Brenda.
Andrew	Take your time, Brenda.
Mrs Wallace	Come on ball, run.
Mr Wallace	She's done it!
Scorer	Brenda Wallace – sixty five. Matthew Thompson – sixty four.
Andrew	She's done it by a point!
Scorer	Brenda Wallace is the champion.

Applause

SCENE: *Brenda's house – next day*

Andrew	What shall we do to celebrate? How about a Chinese?
Brenda	There's one thing I would like to do.
Andrew	What?
Brenda	Go down the snooker hall.
Andrew	Oh, no!
Brenda	Yes, I've got to teach you the game, otherwise . . . .
Andrew	Otherwise what?
Brenda	Otherwise we won't see much of each other. That win has put me in the area finals.

The Experiment

CAST:
Lady Donaldson
Miss Muxlow
Penelope
Shaun
Bill
Jenkins, the gardener and chauffeur

SCENE:
Miss Muxlow's classroom

*Lady Donaldson is lecturing Miss Muxlow;
behind her, looking worried, is her daughter
Penelope.*

Lady D . . . . and I insist that Pen is treated the same
as any other child in your class, Miss Muxlow.
His Lordship and I have discussed the matter
most fully; there is no point in Pen's staying at
a state school for a term unless she mixes with
the other children on terms of absolute
equality. Otherwise there would be little point
in the experiment, would there? Now I mustn't
take up any more of your valuable time, Miss
Muxlow. Now, Pen, remember Jenkins will be
at the school gates at four pm. If there's a little
friend you would like to give a lift to, don't
hesitate. Let her sit in the front with Jenkins.
Do any of you children live in Buckingham
Lane? No, perhaps not.

Miss M Excuse me, Lady Donaldson. Will Penelope be
taking school dinner?

Lady D Certainly. Penelope will eat whatever she's
given for lunch, no matter how awful it is. And
instant coffee is quite adequate for her.

Miss M I'm afraid there's only water at lunchtime.
I suppose I could . . . .

Lady D No, certainly not. Water will be excellent. Her
father drinks water every day.

Penelope But he mixes it with whisky.

Lady D Don't interrupt. Go to your seat.

Miss M William, perhaps you could go to the back.

Bill	You mean me?
Miss M	Yes. Then Penelope could be at the front.
Lady D	Ah, Miss Muxlow. Sorry to be a bore. But that is just what we don't want, isn't it? Pen must not sit at the front . . . . in fact she should sit . . . . next to that boy . . . . the one with the unusual trousers and freckles . . . . he looks exactly the sort Pen should try to understand.
Miss M	That's Shaun, Lady Donaldson.
Lady D	Perfect. Off you go, Pen. Remember, four pm at the school gates.

Lady Donaldson goes out.

Miss M	Now, let us start with Mathematics. Page 153 in your yellow text books. Ah yes, Penelope, the problem of books. Unfortunately, we have to share books. Perhaps I could find one for you though.
Pen	Please don't. I can share this boy's book.
Miss M	Well, I'm not sure. It is rather . . . . I think you'd better take your book home and cover it, Shaun, if you're going to share it with Penelope. But I'll slip out and see if Mrs Rutherford has an extra copy. Meanwhile, you all work the first five problems on page 153.

Miss Muxlow goes out.

Pen	I wish she wouldn't. I don't mind sharing with you. If you don't mind, that is.
Shaun	I don't care.
Pen	You mustn't mind my mother. She's an appalling bore, but she means well.
Shaun	Why should I mind her?
Pen	The reference she made to your trousers.
Shaun	Oh, they're only my scrumping trousers. That's why they're a bit the worse for wear.
Pen	What's scrumping?
Shaun	Nicking fruit.
Pen	And you're planning to go scramping after school?
Shaun	Scrumping, not scramping. Watch out, here comes Muckheap! Get on with these sums.

Miss Muxlow comes back into the classroom.

Miss M	I'm sorry I've been so long, but I have been lucky. A new book for Penelope. Shaun, come and fetch it for her.
Shaun	She ain't got a wooden leg.
Miss M	You insolent animal. Where are your manners, boy? Come and fetch it at once.
Pen	I'd prefer to fetch it myself, Miss Muxlow. I can walk.

SCENE: *Outside the school gates – after school*

Bill	How've you been getting on with Lady Muck then?
Shaun	She's not too bad.
Bill	I been watching you. I reckon you fancy her.
Shaun	No way. Did you see the size of that car she went off in?
Bill	And that bloke with a peaked cap and a face like a pudding.
Shaun	That's Jenkins. He's her chauffeur and gardener.
Bill	Have you got a bag?
Shaun	Yeh, let's get going. Same place as last week?
Bill	Yeh, those big plums should be ripe.
Shaun	I hope they've left the ladder for us again. Very considerate of them.
Bill	It's not climbing the trees I'm worried about – it's getting over that big wall.

SCENE: *In the orchard*

Bill is at the top of a plum tree.

Bill	*(calling)* Hey, I can just see the house. It's like one of those in a Frankenstein film . . . . lots of sticking up bits.
Shaun	Turrets you mean, you fool. You sure there's nobody coming?
Bill	Not a soul in sight. Is that enough?
Shaun	Yeh, come down and help me put 'em in the bag.

Jenkins comes into view with a gun. He shoots off a piece of branch below Bill.

Jenkins Don't move a muscle, either of you hooligans, or you're dead. I've bagged you good and proper.

Shaun is bending down with his right hand full of plums.

Shaun Can't I just straighten up, mister?

Jenkins Just don't move. You're in a good position for horsewhipping, and the other end's just right for potting. He'll fall out of the tree a treat. His Lordship hasn't had any good sport for months. He'll be real chuffed.

Bill You can't touch us. It's against the law.

Jenkins Against the law! What do you think robbing people's orchards is?

Shaun We was only after a bit of fruit.

Jenkins Fruit? You'll get fruit all right.

Penelope comes towards them.

Pen Jenkins! Whatever do you think you're doing?

Jenkins Caught two hooligans poaching, Miss.

Pen Hooligans! They're my guests. I invited them. You really have excelled yourself this time, Jenkins.

Jenkins Now, Miss, I'm sure Her Ladyship wouldn't approve of you telling fibs like that. You asking me to believe you invited these two hooligans, Miss?

Pen I'm not asking you anything, Jenkins. I'm telling you. Put your silly gun away, and go and dig or do something useful.

Jenkins stalks off.

Shaun, will you straighten up, please? I know they're only your scrumping trousers, but they don't show you off to your best advantage from that position. And you, Bill is it? Come down from that tree.

Shaun	Thanks for not turning us in.
Pen	I think you two must be off your chumps. If you'd wanted fruit I could have brought you some.
Bill	It ain't the plums really. Well, it's a bit the plums, but it's mostly the excitement – that we might get caught.
Pen	Well, I hope you've had enough excitement today! Jenkins was right. My father's mad enough to horsewhip you or shoot you. That would have been exciting, wouldn't it?
Shaun	Well, we'd better get off back over the wall. See you tomorrow.
Pen	You'd much better go out of the front gate, and be quick about it. If you get stuck on the wall, Jenkins will certainly pot you.
Bill	But you've scooted him off.
Pen	Not easily done. He's gone to my mother, if I know him – which I do. 'Is you aware, m'lady, that Miss Penelope is consorting with a pair of hooligans?' So take yourselves off through that gate, as quickly as you can.
Bill	Too late. There's somebody coming.
Pen	Oh cripes! It's Mummy with the vile Jenkins.
Shaun	We'll run for it.
Pen	And be shot. Quickly, help me pull this lid off.
Bill	What is it?
Pen	A well.
Shaun	I'd as soon be shot as drowned.
Pen	There's no water in it. Come on, in you go. It's only two metres deep. My grandfather dug it to draw water for the kitchen garden. After two metres, he died.
Bill	It stinks in here.
Pen	It's damp earth, not my grandfather. He was taken out. Are you in, Shaun?
Pen	I'm coming in as well. I don't want to be cross-examined, until some of the fire's gone from Mummy's breath.

Lady D and Jenkins enter

Lady D	I hope we're not chasing wild geese, Jenkins.
Jenkins	No, Ma'am. It was definitely two boys.

Lady D Well, there's no sign of them now, or of my daughter.

Jenkins Shush, m'lady.

Lady D Don't you shush me, Jenkins.

Jenkins Sorry, m'lady. I think I heard 'em. In there!

Lady D In Percy's well?

Jenkins Yes, Madam.

Lady D Off with the lid then, man. If there really are a brace of urchins in there, we can nail down the lid and send for the magistrates.

Jenkins pulls off the lid.

Pen It's only me, Mummy.

Lady D looks in.

Lady D It is not only you, Pen. Were it only you, it would be understandable. Lunacy is rampant on your father's side of the family and solitary occupation of redundant wells would be a relatively harmless sign of madness. What have you in there with you?

Pen It's Shaun. He's a boy from . . . .

Lady D Out you climb, the pair of you. Good God, am I too late? What's the matter with your trousers, boy?

Shaun They're just a bit big, Missus. They slip a bit . . . .

Lady D Good Lord, so they are. Where in heaven's name did you find this boy, Penelope?

Pen I sit with him at school, Mummy. You told me to, if you remember.

Lady D Vaguely, yes. I do recall those remarkable trousers. However, I cannot recall instructing you to sit with him at the bottom of well holes.

Pen You said I was to mix with people such as Shaun.

Lady D Not socially, you fool. And certainly not in compromising positions in well-holes. Now, out you come. Good heavens, I refuse to believe the evidence of my eyes. I do believe there's another one. Am I right, Jenkins?

Jenkins	Yes, Ma'am. Miss Penelope was sitting on him. Trying to conceal him, if you ask me.
Lady D	At least this one's trousers seem to be in a relatively conventional position.
Bill	We're off home, Missus. You can say what you like.
Lady D	You insolent creature! Jenkins, shoot him.
Jenkins	Certainly, Ma'am.
Pen	Don't be ridiculous, Mother.
Lady D	Be quiet you . . . . you . . . . you father's daughter. That's what you are. Started his habits early, eh? Jenkins, take her away. You urchins, I'll give you the same chance as I'd give a fox. You have thirty seconds before Jenkins starts shooting. Bolt for your holes!

Bill and Shaun run.

SCENE:	*Miss Muxlow's classroom – the next morning*

Lady Donaldson bursts in.

Lady D	Where are you hiding my daughter, woman?
Miss M	I beg your pardon. Penelope hasn't turned up.
Lady D	Blighter's run orf. If she turns up here, you're to ring me immediately. You understand?
Miss M	Isn't she to continue her lessons here?
Lady D	Of course not. That's orf. Stupid idea. Her father's – not mine. Man's an idiot! Still, I did think it would take longer than one day for her to be infected. Where's the Headmistress? I need to give her her instructions.
Miss M	I'll take you there.

Miss Muxlow and Lady Donaldson go out.

Bill	Do you know where she is?
Shaun	She's on the train to London by now. She spent last night in our garden shed. Said she was running away from home.
Bill	Does your Mum . . . .?
Shaun	Shush. She don't know.
Bill	You can't blame her, running off from that old bag.

Shaun   She'll be back, I expect.

Bill   You mean, you hope. I knew you fancied her.

Shaun   Don't be stupid.

Bill   You've gone red round your freckles.

The Collectors

CAST:
Pete
Carol
Tracy
Glenn
Wayne
Dawn
Mr Hunt
Miss Swann
Mrs Jones
Mrs Brown
Mr Brown

SCENE: *Lonely countryside*

The children are out for an adventure walk with teachers. It is raining hard.

Miss Swann	Isn't there somewhere we can shelter?
Mr Hunt	Not until we get to the village.
Mrs Jones	How far is that?
Mr Hunt	Nearly three miles.
Dawn	Three miles!
Tracy	I'm soaked.
Miss Swann	The children are getting very wet.
Mr Hunt	I can't help that. We'll just have to press on.
Pete	Can't we shelter over there, sir?
Mr Hunt	Where?
Pete	There. In that house.
Mr Hunt	That's not a house, surely? Hard to see in all this rain.
Miss Swann	Of course it is. Try wiping your glasses.
Mr Hunt	You're right. Lonely place to choose for a house. It certainly wasn't there when I was here walking last summer.
Mrs Jones	Funny looking place.
Miss Swann	Are we just going to stand here in the downpour gaping at it?
Dawn	Yes, can't we go up there and ask for shelter, sir?

Mr Hunt	We can't take all you crowd into a private house. You're dripping wet.
Mrs Jones	There's probably a shed or garage. We could shelter there.
Miss Swann	We can at least ask.
Wayne	Yes, sir. Why not?
Tracy	I'm freezing.
Mr Hunt	Oh, all right.

SCENE: *Inside the kitchen of the house*

Mrs Brown is standing with all the children and teachers. Mr Brown comes in through the outer door.

Mr Brown	I've hung up all the wet clothing in the porch.
Mr Hunt	I don't know why I'm still holding this walking stick.
Mr Brown	Give it to me. I'll put it outside with the other things.
Mr Hunt	It's all right. I'll hang it on the back of this chair.
Mrs Brown	Now that we've all introduced ourselves, why don't you children sit down?
Mr Brown	And the grown-ups can come through into the sitting room.
Mrs Brown	You children will be all right here, won't you? There isn't room through there for everyone.
Carol	Yes, thanks.
Glenn	Oh, yes.
Pete	We'll be fine.
Mrs Jones	Thank you very much for taking us in like this.
Mr Brown	Our pleasure.
Mrs Brown	There's a fresh pot of tea made in the other room. Would you like a cup?
Miss Swann	I'd love one.
Mrs Jones	So would I.
Mrs Brown	Would you like to come through, then?

Mr and Mrs Brown and the three teachers go out. The children are silent for a moment or two, looking round.

Wayne   You can't hear any sound of that wind in here.
Tracy   No. It's terribly quiet. Weird.
Dawn   I can just hear their voices in the sitting room.
Glenn   It's cold in here too.
Wayne   Maybe we feel cold because we're tired from all that walking.
Tracy   And we did get wet.
Glenn   No. Not just that. It is cold.
Pete   And empty. This kitchen reminds me of a hospital. Where do they wash up?
Dawn   In the sink.
Tracy   Or the washing-up machine.
Pete   There's nothing like that.
Carol   There's nothing standing about, either. No plates. No pots and pans. Things like that.
Dawn   They'll be put away in cupboards.

Wayne opens a cupboard near the back door.

Wayne   This one's quite empty.
Dawn   Don't go poking about, Wayne.

Pete opens the fridge door.

Pete   There's nothing at all in this fridge. And the light's not on. It's not even working.
Tracy   Leave things alone, you two. It's cheeky to snoop. Besides, they might come in and catch you.
Carol   I thought there was something a bit strange about Mr and Mrs Brown.
Pete   Funny you should say that, so did I.
Glenn   Perhaps they're crooks. This is their hide-out.
Tracy   They'd hardly have let us in if they were crooks, would they?
Dawn   No. That's silly.
Carol   Maybe we ought to have gone on walking to the village.
Dawn   We'd have got drenched.

Mrs Brown comes back into the room.

Mrs Brown   All right here? Good.

She notices the partly open cupboard door.

Oh – were you looking for something in that cupboard?

Dawn It was Wayne. He was being nosy.

Mrs Brown I see.

She closes the door, looking at Wayne.

Wayne I didn't mean any harm. We just wondered where you put your plates and things.

Mrs Brown I'd rather you didn't touch anything. We've just moved in and haven't had time to sort things out. That's why this place looks rather deserted.

Pete We only wondered—

Mrs Brown Yes. Well – would you all like a drink?

Tracy I would.

Glenn Me, too.

Mrs Brown Will orange juice be all right?

Wayne Yes, please.

Dawn Fine. Thanks.

The others nod.

Mrs Brown Good. And remember – please leave these cupboards alone.

Wayne We will.

Pete Don't worry, Mrs Brown.

Mrs Brown Hmmm.

She looks at the closed doors of a larger cupboard on the opposite wall.

Do remember that. I'll go and get those drinks.

She goes out.

Carol Did you see her hand?

Dawn No. What?

Carol When she closed that cupboard door. She has seven fingers. On both hands. I looked.

Tracy Ugh! Horrid!

Pete I was watching her eyes.

Glenn	Yes. Far as I could see they were all one colour. They didn't have any black – sort of – centres.
Wayne	Go on. She could be something weird like a vampire.
Tracy	Oh, shut up!
Dawn	Yes, shut up. You're making all this up to scare us.
Pete	No, we're not.
Tracy	I don't want to stay here.
Wayne	I'll tell you something. That rain has changed to thick fog outside. I've been watching it.
Glenn	Yes. You can't see anything out of that window.
Carol	No. I hope it doesn't mean we're going to have to stay here all night.
Tracy	Stay here? All night? Not me.
Dawn	I don't fancy that, either. Let's go.
Glenn	We can't just slide off.
Pete	I'll go and tell Mr Hunt and the others how we feel.

He goes out.

Wayne	It is all a bit mysterious. I wonder what's in that other cupboard.
Dawn	Leave it alone.
Tracy	If she catches you, she'll be mad.
Wayne	She won't catch me.

He opens the cupboard door. Behind it are dials, digital read-outs, coloured lights and a mass of other electronic equipment.

Glenn	What on earth is all that doing there?
Wayne	Is it some kind of computer?
Carol	Those things – are they figures or words?
Glenn	Some kind of foreign language.
Tracy	Look at all those lights!
Dawn	It's real space age stuff.
Glenn	What could it be for?
Wayne	Spying.
Glenn	You think so?
Carol	Close the door. Someone's coming.

They close the door but it doesn't quite shut.
Pete comes back in.

Pete	I think we need help.
Carol	What did Mr Hunt say?
Pete	Nothing. He couldn't.
Wayne	Couldn't?
Pete	I went quietly. I was a bit scared. The door of the other room was partly open. I saw Mr Hunt first, sitting there – not moving – staring at nothing.
Glenn	You mean he was thinking about something? He was tired.
Pete	No, I do not. He was drugged. Miss Swann and Mrs Jones are the same. I crept a bit closer. Then I could see them, too. They were sitting there – blank – as if they'd been turned to stone.
Carol	And Mr and Mrs Brown?
Pete	They were looking at them and – I don't know – talking.
Carol	What were they saying?
Pete	No idea. They weren't really talking. It sounded – they were just sort of hissing and clicking at each other.
Tracy	I want to get out of here.
Wayne	I am getting out – right now!

He goes to the back door and tries to open it.

	It's locked. There's no key.
Dawn	Let me try. No. It just won't open.
Glenn	How about the window?

Wayne tries the window.

Wayne	No chance. It won't move.
Tracy	Smash the glass! We've got to get out!
Carol	Here. Try Mr Hunt's walking stick. Use that, Wayne.

Wayne tries to break the glass with the stick.

Wayne	It won't break.

He hits the glass again.

It just bounces off.

Glenn Let me try.

He takes the walking stick and uses it.

It's no use. That glass is like steel.

Pete Come on. We'll see if there's a way out through the front.

They begin to crowd towards the kitchen door when Mrs Brown comes in with a tray of drinks.

Mrs Brown Good heavens! What's all this row? What on earth have you children been doing?

Carol We want to leave.

Mrs Brown In this fog? How can you?

Pete What have you done to Mr Hunt and the others?

Mrs Brown Done? Nothing. We've been having a cup of tea.

Carol Pete says you've drugged them.

Mrs Brown Nonsense! Where in the world did you get that idea?

She notices the cupboard left partly open.

I do wish you'd have the courtesy not to interfere with these cupboards.

Glenn What is that stuff in there?

Mrs Brown What do you mean 'stuff'? It's electronic equipment. It belongs to my husband. He's a scientist. It's part of his work.

Pete And why is the back door locked?

Mrs Brown It always locks when you close it. It's a burglar-proof lock. The windows are burglar-proof, too. My husband doesn't want to run the risk of having any expensive equipment stolen.

Tracy They've been trying to scare us – saying there was something strange about this house and about you.

Mrs Brown	How dare you? After we've taken you in and looked after you! After I've gone to the trouble of getting these drinks for you! The least you can do is to sit quietly and drink them.
Pete	I bet they're drugged. Just like the tea you gave Mr Hunt and the others.
Mrs Brown	Now – just stop that kind of talk!
Pete	I saw them. You've got them in the other room – drugged.
Mrs Brown	You saw nothing of the sort. They're all chatting to Mr Brown right now.
Carol	Ask them to come in here then, so we can see them.
Mrs Brown	Certainly not. I'm not dragging them in here just because of a lot of children's silly fantasies.
Glenn	Well – let us go in there and see them.
Mrs Brown	No you don't. I'm not going to be ordered about by children.

She bars the way through the door.

Carol	She can't stop us on her own if we all try to go.
Mrs Brown	All right! All right! I'll go and fetch one of your teachers. Stupid children!

She goes out.

Dawn	See! She's going to bring them.
Tracy	They aren't drugged at all. You were trying to scare us.
Dawn	You're stupid you are, Pete. Stupid!
Tracy	It's an ordinary house and they're ordinary people.
Dawn	Frightening us like that! You're rotten!
Pete	I know what I saw. Give us that walking stick, Glenn.
Glenn	Here you are.

As Glenn gives Pete the stick, both Mr and Mrs Brown come in.

Carol	Where's Mr Hunt?
Mr Brown	He won't be coming. And you had better drink.

Pete	Don't! Don't anybody touch that stuff!
Mr Brown	It will make no difference. You can't escape, anyway.
Wayne	Oh no? Come on, Glenn. Let's get past them.
Glenn	Right.

He and Wayne make a rush for the door. One-armed, Mrs Brown brushes them away. They are sent flying across the kitchen.

Mr Brown	Stop that! We don't want any of you damaged. And either one of us alone is more than a match for any five feeble Earth children.
Carol	If you try to keep us here, the police will come looking for us.
Mr Brown	Will they? They won't find you. You're going away.
Tracy	No! Where are you taking us?
Mrs Brown	Shall I tell them?
Mr Brown	Why not? It might calm them to know there's no avoiding their fate.
Mrs Brown	We're taking you to our home planet.
Glenn	Home planet?
Carol	You're not from Earth? You're aliens.
Mr Brown	Exactly.
Wayne	But you're human. You look human.
Mrs Brown	We can take on any shape we wish – for a time. So can our spaceship.
Mr Brown	At the moment, as you have seen, it looks like an Earth house – very useful for our mission.
Mrs Brown	In a few moments we shall convert it to a spaceship again and return to our normal shape.
Mr Brown	So you had better drink. It will make the shock of take-off easier for you.
Tracy	But you mustn't take us. You can't!
Mr Brown	How wrong you are.
Wayne	But why us? Why pick on us?
Mrs Brown	You were available. We collect creatures from other worlds like you.
Carol	Why? What for?
Mr Brown	For experiment and scientific study. You will be useful to us.
Pete	Oh no we won't.

*Flinging the cupboard door open, Pete holds up
the walking stick, two-handed.*

	Come one step nearer and I smash this equipment.
Mr Brown	No!
Mrs Brown	Do nothing yet. Too dangerous!
Pete	Grab a chair, Glenn, and come over here. If they so much as move – smash all this!
Glenn	Right.

He joins Pete with the chair raised and ready.

Mr Brown	Smash any parts of those panels and you can kill us all.
Pete	I'll take that chance. Carol. You and the rest get near that outer door.
Carol	Yes. Come on, you lot. Quick!

*All the children, except Pete and Glenn, cluster
against the door to the outside.*

Mr Brown	They're only children. We can rush them. Attack!
Mrs Brown	No. They're wild. Keep still!
Mr Brown	We can't let this happen. Beaten by inferior creatures!
Mrs Brown	We must. If they break any part of that equipment, we are stranded here on Earth. We can do no repairs here.
Pete	You! Go and bring Mr Hunt and the others out here.
Mr Brown	No.

*Pete taps the panel with the stick and swings it
back for a real blow.*

Mrs Brown	Go! Go and fetch them!

Mr Brown goes out.

Pete	You! How do we open the back door and the door in the porch?
Mrs Brown	Yes. All right. It's that control down there on

the left. It's marked with a yellow light. Press
it.

Glenn Don't trust her, Pete.

Pete I won't. Listen – if those doors don't open at
once, Glenn and I start wrecking!

Mrs Brown I'm telling the truth. Press the control. Press
it.

Pete Watch her, Glenn. And – if this is a trick – use
that chair.

Glenn Don't you worry, mate.

Pete presses the control and the doors open.

Carol It's all right, Pete. It worked.

*Mr Hunt, Miss Swann and Mrs Jones stagger
dazedly into the room. Mr Brown is behind
them.*

Pete Help them. Get them outside and well away
from the house.

Wayne What about you?

Pete Don't worry. Get going.

*The children help the adults out through the
back door, leaving Pete and Glenn facing Mr
and Mrs Brown.*

Glenn What now, Pete? They'll grab us as we run for
it.

Pete No, they won't. I've got a plan. You go first.

Glenn Not without you.

Mrs Brown We underestimated these creatures. They were
never so fierce before.

Mr Brown They were all drugged before.

Pete Go through that other door behind you and
close it!

Mr Brown And – if we refuse?

Pete You'll be very sorry.

He taps the panel again with the stick.

Mrs Brown Do as he says. Quickly. We've no choice.

The two aliens go out and close the door behind them.

Pete Run for it, Glenn. Now!
Glenn Right.

Glenn and Pete dash for the back door and disappear through it.

SCENE: *Moorland – a little later*

The whole party are sitting on the grass. It is neither raining nor foggy. The sun is out.

Mrs Jones I can't believe any of it.
Carol But you remember being drugged, Miss, don't you?
Dawn And all our anoraks were left in that house spaceship thing.
Glenn And the house isn't there any more.
Pete Just vanished in a soundless flash.
Miss Swann I know! I know! But it's mad. It's incredible.
Mr Hunt We have to report it.
Miss Swann Don't be silly! How can we? It'll sound utter nonsense.
Mr Hunt People disappear. Maybe they were – collected – as we were. Surely we've got to tell the story – believable or not – as a warning.
Wayne It'll sound crazy.
Tracy I don't want people thinking I'm potty.
Mrs Jones I agree. Say nothing.
Mr Hunt I don't know. Swear everybody to secrecy? Anyway, I'm cold. Let's get on down to the village. Talk it over as we go, eh?

The party moves off, arguing.

A Day at the Seaside?

CAST:	**Mum**
	Dad
	Jim
	Linda
	Sandra
	Ted
	Policeman
	Policewoman
SCENE:	*Jim's and Linda's flat – morning*

Mum	Hurry up, Dad.
Dad	I am hurrying.
Mum	We'll never get there.
Dad	Yes we will. Couple of hours. Easy.
Jim	There'll be others on the road.
Dad	Not at this time of day.
Linda	What about Ted?
Jim	I told him to be here at eight sharp.
Linda	Well, it's gone that.
Jim	He'll be here.
Mum	Dad, you haven't shaved yet.
Dad	I'm going to – right away.
Jim	Sandra's not here either.
Linda	She said she wouldn't be late.

The front doorbell rings.

Ah, I expect that's her.

She goes to the front door and opens it.

Sandra	Sorry I'm late. I didn't hear the alarm.
Linda	That's all right. Dad hasn't shaved yet.
Sandra	I slept right through it.
Mum	Hello, Sandra. Just pack the sandwiches, Linda, while I make the tea. It should be a lovely day. The sun's breaking through.
Linda	Good.

54

SCENE: *In the street by the car – a short while later*

Jim Where is Ted?

Dad If he's not here in five minutes, we're off.

Mum Are you sure you can take six in a car?

Dad Easy. Jim can go behind the back seat. He can look after the grub.

Jim Thank you. What about Linda?

Mum Jim!

Dad Or you can take it in turns with Ted.

Jim If he comes. Just like him to be late.

Mum Did you pack the flask, Linda?

Linda Don't worry, Mum. Everything's in the bag.

Dad Blast! I've left my tobacco in the flat. Run up and get it for me, Jim.

Jim Why me? What about Linda?

Mum You run and get it, Jim.

Jim Always me.

He slumps off.

Sandra Will it be cold by the sea? I hope this jumper is enough.

Mum It'll be a lovely day. The clouds are clearing.

Linda I'm wearing the same. You'll be all right.

Sandra Here's Ted.

Ted Sorry I'm late. I couldn't find my shoes.

Dad We were just going without you. If I hadn't left my tobacco, we'd have gone.

Mum Dad!

Dad Now have we got everything?

Mum Of course we have. Don't you trust me?

Dad Of course I do, dear. Right. All aboard.

Mum What about Jim?

Dad He can get in last. I've got to close the door for him.

Jim runs back.

Jim Is this it?

Dad Yes, it's a new packet. In you get.

Jim There's not much room.

Dad Stop complaining. Right. Seaside, here we come.

55

Mum	What about petrol? Have we enough?
Dad	Don't you trust me?
Mum	Oh well, I remember that time . . . .
Dad	Don't you trust me?
Mum	Of course.
Jim	Oh!
Mum	What is it?
Jim	I think I've sat on the flask.
Mum	Oh, Jim, you haven't!
Jim	It's going through my jeans.
Ted	You wet!
Jim	Shut up, Ted!
Dad	Get out, you idiot!
Jim	Well, there wasn't much room in there. I'm too big to be squashed in there. Linda should have sat there.
Dad	There was still no need to sit on the flask. Look at my car.
Mum	It'll clean up. But we haven't got another flask. Oh look! It's soaked right through the sandwiches. Now I've got to make some more.
Dad	No you're not. We can buy sandwiches when we get there. We don't want to waste any more time. What a family!
Jim	I couldn't help it.
Mum	Nobody's blaming you. They'll be expensive to buy at the seaside.
Dad	Never mind that. We don't go every week. Now then, if you'll all get in, off we'll go – at last.
Mum	We can't go with that mess in the back. Jim can't sit there, I'll go and get a cloth.
Linda	I'll get it.
Dad	I've got the window cloth here. Use that.
Linda	I'll do it.
Dad	One day – just one day – this family is going to do something without any hitch, fuss or bother. But it won't be till you two have left home.
Jim	I tell you I couldn't help it.
Mum	Dad's not blaming you.
Dad	I am.
Linda	There, that's all right. You can get back in, Jim.

Dad   Right. Once more, off we go.

Mum   Just a minute. What about Gus? Where was he?

Jim   I don't know.

Mum   We can't leave him shut in a bedroom. He'll make such a mess.

Jim   We should have brought him with us.

Dad   I'm not having six and that dog in here.

Jim   Go on, Dad, he can squeeze in with me.

Dad   I thought you were complaining about lack of room. No, I made it quite clear last night. No dog.

Mum   Go and make sure all the doors are open and he's got plenty of water.

Jim   Me again! Why can't Linda?

Dad   He's your dog.

Jim   Always me.

He slouches off again.

Ted   I'll come with you.

Dad   You stay here now you're in. I'll just see how the engine sounds.

Mum   You're not suggesting there's anything wrong with the car, are you? You spent all yesterday on it.

Dad   There you are. It's started. Oh. Sounds a bit rough.

Mum   Dad.

Dad   It started well enough yesterday. It ran well too.

Mum   Why did you suggest going to the seaside if there's something wrong with the car?

Dad   There can't be anything wrong with the car.

Linda   Listen to it.

Sandra   We do seem to be having our problems.

Linda   That's putting it mildly.

Ted   Shall I give it a push?

Dad   No.

Jim returns.

Jim   What's up now?

Linda   There's something wrong with the engine.

Jim	Oh no!
Mum	You should have been up earlier and tested the car before I made all the sandwiches.
Dad	Don't nag!
Linda	It'll be all right, Mum. We'll have our day by the seaside.
Ted	Or we can always go on the common by the duck pond.
Jim	Can I help?
Dad	No.

SCENE: *The same – half an hour later*

Dad	Would you imagine it! After all that it was just a loose plug lead. I thought I'd checked them all.
Mum	It's too late to go now. It'll be stop and start all the way.
Dad	We are going. And that's final. Right.

A police car pulls up and a policeman and policewoman get out.

	What is it?
Policewoman	Excuse me, sir. Were you thinking of driving this car with five passengers?
Dad	Plenty of room for them.
Policewoman	Yes, sir, but the car's not designed for six. It's dangerous.
Dad	I'm a careful driver. I don't go fast.
Policeman	Then I'll have to warn you, sir, that it's an offence to drive an overladen vehicle.
Ted	Okay. I'll not go. I don't mind.
Jim	I'm not going without you, Ted.
Dad	What a country! Why don't you catch some criminals instead of messing up our day's outing?
Policewoman	It's for your own safety, sir.
Sandra	I'll stay back here with you, Jim.
Linda	I'm not going to be the only one going.
Mum	It's too late now anyway.
Linda	You go with Dad, Mum. You'll enjoy it.

Mum No, I won't. I like to go out with you children some times. He'll only go to sleep when we get there. What fun is that for me?

Dad I won't.

Mum Come on, I'll make us all a cup of coffee.

Dad Thank you. What a family! What a day at the seaside!

On Trial

CAST: **Gary Parker**, older brother
Steve Parker, younger brother
Linda, their younger sister
Uncle Ken, their great uncle
Mrs Parker, mother and schoolteacher
Mr Parker, father
Mrs Wilson, teacher at the same school as Mrs Parker

SCENE: *The Parkers' living room*

Steve is alone. Gary comes in.

Gary I'm sick of that stinking job. Sick of it!
Steve Better than being on the dole though, isn't it?
Gary Fat lot you know, our kid. What are you grinning at?
Steve I wasn't.
Gary No? What's so funny then?
Steve I've got a trial with City.
Gary You've what?
Steve They want me to play in a trial game.
Gary I know what a trial is, berk. Who says so?
Steve They phoned old Brooker at school.

Linda comes in.

Linda Hey, our Steve! Vikki says you're going to play for City. Chris told her.
Steve Playing? I don't know about that. I've got a trial with them.
Linda You haven't! When?
Steve Soon. Brooker told me. There's a letter coming.
Linda Great! Striker for City, eh?
Gary Some hopes.
Linda Don't be so mean, Gary. How many people get a chance like this?
Uncle Ken *(calling from outside)* Anybody home?
Linda In here, Uncle Ken.

60

Uncle Ken comes in.

Uncle Ken I've brought some veg from the allotment. Left it on the kitchen table. Where's your mum?

Steve She's probably working late at school again.

Linda Here! Uncle Ken–Steve's going to play for City.

Uncle Ken Never! You've done it then, have you? Good lad. Well, I'm blowed.

Gary Playing in a trial's nothing. Getting taken on is something else.

Uncle Ken City! They're still a great team. Always have been. I can remember as a kid before the war . . . .

Gary Rubbish! They're even falling out of the Second Division.

Uncle Ken You don't know what you're talking about. They won their last two games.

Gary Playing Cardiff and Notts County. So what?

Linda You're just jealous, Gary.

Gary Jealous? Me? Don't talk soft.

Uncle Ken What does your Mum say?

Steve I haven't told her yet. Haven't had time.

Uncle Ken Oh.

Gary Lot of fuss about a game of football. Isn't anyone going to make us a cup of tea? I've been working.

Uncle Ken When is the big day?

Steve I don't know exactly. It'll be within a week or two.

Linda You'll probably get to meet some of the players.

Uncle Ken I'd have given my right arm for a chance like that when I was your age, Steve. If it hadn't been for the war—

Gary I'm going up to have a wash.

He goes out.

Steve What do you think I should say to Mum?

Uncle Ken Just tell her, lad. I mean – it's a triumph, isn't it? She'll see it your way.

Steve I hope so.

Linda *(at the window)* She's coming in the gate now.

Uncle Ken	Look, Steve – it could be a bit tricky. Do you want me to speak to her?
Steve	No. I'll go and let her in. I'll tell her.

He goes out.

Linda	Smashing, isn't it?
Uncle Ken	Out of this world. His Mum must see that.

SCENE: *The same room – a few days later*

Mr and Mrs Parker are sitting with Steve. Linda is at the window.

Linda	It's Uncle Ken. He's coming in the back way.
Mrs Parker	I thought so. We can do without him putting his oar in.
Mr Parker	Have a heart, Peg. He's very interested.

Uncle Ken comes in.

Uncle Ken	Hello there. Have you heard?
Steve	Yes. It's next Wednesday.
Uncle Ken	Best of luck then. That's great.
Steve	It could have been.
Uncle Ken	Why? What's up?
Steve	It's Mum.
Uncle Ken	Ah, Peg! You're not spoiling it for him, are you?
Mrs Parker	I'm not spoiling it for him. I'm trying to make him see sense. He's talking of leaving school.
Uncle Ken	Well – if they offer him a place, he'll probably have to, won't he?
Mrs Parker	He's not leaving school. We've had all that with Gary. Steve's got exams to pass. With his brains he could go to university.
Uncle Ken	And then? Jobcentres are full of people with degrees nowadays.
Mrs Parker	That's nonsense. And I don't really see that it's got much to do with you.
Uncle Ken	I'm only putting a point of view.
Mrs Parker	We don't need it. We can look after our children without interference, thank you.
Uncle Ken	I'm not interfering. I'm trying to show you

how Steve might see it.

Mrs Parker I know how Steve sees it. We've talked of nothing else since I heard. Football! Can't you ever think of anything else?

Uncle Ken Well – you needn't bite my head off.

Mr Parker Yes. Hang on, Peg. There's no need to fly off the handle. You see – what she thinks, Ken – what we both think – is this—

Mrs Parker I've seen Gary throw everything up and land in a dead-end job with no qualifications. Steve's not doing that. He's going on to 'A' levels and college.

Steve I'm not. If I get a chance, I'm joining City.

Mrs Parker You're staying at school.

Mr Parker Look, lad – I've told you before – forget the glamour. Even if you did get taken on, you'd be an apprentice – a trainee. You'd be cleaning boots and sweeping the terraces.

Uncle Ken That's only part of it. If he's got the talent – and I know he has – he could make the first team.

Steve I could play for England – how about that?

Mr Parker From a Second Division club? You'd be much more likely to spend your life playing for the reserves.

Mrs Parker And what sort of a job would you get then, when you were too old to play? You'd know nothing but kicking a ball about.

Steve If I made the first team, I'd make enough money to do what I liked. Run a business. Live in comfort.

Mrs Parker Would you now? Listen. You've pestered and pestered us into letting you go for that trial. Two more words from you and it's off. We were silly to agree to it in the first place.

Steve You can't stop me going.

Mrs Parker Oh yes we can.

Steve How? By locking me up?

He moves towards the door.

Mrs Parker Where are you off now?

Steve Out.

Mrs Parker Have you done your homework?

Steve   Yes.

He goes out.

Uncle Ken   Let him go. You'll do more harm than good going on at him like this.

Linda   I think you're mean.

Mrs Parker   You be quiet!

Mr Parker   You could be right, Ken. The more we argue, the more obstinate he gets.

Uncle Ken   I wouldn't push too hard. I mean – he might not be any good in the trial. Then all this fuss would be for nothing.

Linda   You're all against him. I'm going to find him.

She goes out.

Mr Parker   I've never known him so thick-headed over anything before. There's no reasoning with him.

Uncle Ken   He has taken it to heart. You know, Peg, you can't live that boy's life for him.

Mrs Parker   Hmm. He'll thank me in the end. Anyway, I've better things to do than to go on and on about it. I've got all those cards to get ready for school tomorrow.

She goes out.

SCENE: *The Parkers' kitchen – a few days later*

Mrs Parker comes in with Mrs Wilson.

Mrs Parker   Thanks for the lift. Will you have a cup of tea?

Mrs Wilson   I'd love one. I'm tired. Those kids in my class take it out of me.

Mrs Parker   Sometimes I think you're lucky not to have any of your own at home.

Mrs Wilson   Sounds as though yours are giving you a hard time.

Mrs Parker   Linda's all right. She's still a kid. Gary's a worry. But there's not much we can do about him now. It's Steve.

Mrs Wilson	What's he done?
Mrs Parker	He wants to leave school. He's been offered a trial with City. It's a chance to join the team as an apprentice.
Mrs Wilson	I thought he was going to college.
Mrs Parker	He is, if I have anything to do with it.
Mrs Wilson	But football's what he wants?
Mrs Parker	He's too young to know what he wants. I mean – Geoff and I have made a lot of sacrifices for those kids. Gary insisted on leaving school. Look how that's turned out. And Steve's a lot cleverer than Gary.
Mrs Wilson	Hmm. You know Beth Rogers?
Mrs Parker	Yes.
Mrs Wilson	Their son Wayne, was keen to go in the army. They wouldn't hear of it. You know how anti-war Beth is. And they were scared of what might happen to him if he ended up in Northern Ireland.
Mrs Parker	But he's working in an office now.
Mrs Wilson	He was. He couldn't stand it and left. There was no end of a row at home about that. Then he drifted about, working for a builder and being on the dole. There were more rows.
Mrs Parker	Silly lad.
Mrs Wilson	In the end he suddenly cleared off – down to London, they think. They haven't heard much from him. They think he might have joined the army, after all. He's old enough.
Mrs Parker	But that's terrible. How could he treat his parents like that?
Mrs Wilson	Beth's very upset. She thinks it's her fault.
Mrs Parker	That's stupid.
Mrs Wilson	Sometimes it's sensible to let children go their own way.
Mrs Parker	Jill – you aren't the best judge. You haven't got any children.
Mrs Wilson	No. I was only saying—
Mrs Parker	I'm sure Steve's not a bit like Wayne. Anyway, the tea's ready. You like a lot of milk, don't you?
Mrs Wilson	Please.

SCENE:	*The Parkers' living room – the day of the trial*
	Mr and Mrs Parker, Gary, Linda and Uncle Ken are waiting for Steve to come back from the trial game.
Mrs Parker	I wonder where he's been till this time.
	Steve comes in. He is limping.
	You're very late.
Steve	I've twisted a knee. They took me in for an X-ray.
Linda	You haven't broken anything!
Steve	No. It hurts a bit but there's no harm done.
Uncle Ken	How did it happen?
Steve	I got tangled up with one of the defenders. It's nothing.
Mrs Parker	It might have been really serious.
Steve	You'd have liked that, wouldn't you? You'd be glad if I'd done something to put me out of the game for good.
Mrs Parker	What a thing to say!
Uncle Ken	Anyway – how did you get on?
Steve	I don't know.
Gary	You must have some idea.
Steve	I missed my one chance at goal. I misplaced a couple of passes. I didn't do well.
Linda	Poor Steve!
Mrs Parker	Well – it's all over now.
Steve	Oh, I knew you'd be pleased. You're really glad to see me fail, aren't you?
Mr Parker	That's no way to speak to your mother.
Steve	It's true. Win or lose I knew that it was going to come to nothing. She's made that very clear. I'd had all the heart taken out of me before I began.
Gary	Excuses, eh? On the day you just weren't good enough.
Steve	Who's asking you? What have you ever done?
Gary	I've gone my own way, mate.
Steve	And where has it got you?
Gary	At least I don't blame others for what's happened to me.

Linda	Oh yes you do. You blame everybody.
Mr Parker	That's enough of that.
Uncle Ken	It's rough luck, lad. You'll get over it though.
Steve	Will I?
Mrs Parker	Of course you will.
Steve	It's nothing to you, is it? I won't forget the way you've been.
Mrs Parker	We let you take the trial. You had your chance and it hasn't worked out.
Steve	I had no chance. I could have played a blinder. It wouldn't have got me anywhere with you standing in the way. How do you think I felt when I walked out on to that field?
Mr Parker	You'll just have to accept it, Steve.
Mrs Parker	Yes. Now you can give all your mind to school work. You can think about your real future.
Steve	Future? What future?

He goes out.

Mr Parker	He's taken it hard, Peg.
Uncle Ken	You never know how strongly a quiet lad can feel about things.
Mrs Parker	He'll see things differently tomorrow.
SCENE:	*The Parkers' living room – a few evenings later*

Mr Parker and Uncle Ken are sitting together.

Uncle Ken	How did he react when the letter came?
Mr Parker	He didn't. He's been funny all these last few days. He's had one real bust-up with his mother. Since then he's hardly spoken. She's upset.
Uncle Ken	To be expected. What was the row about?
Mr Parker	The usual. He said she had no confidence in him. All she wanted was her own way. She'd no idea what he was like as a player and she knew nothing about football.
Uncle Ken	That's not far wrong. Has she ever watched him play?
Mr Parker	She could have done. I have, once or twice.
Uncle Ken	Only once or twice? And you don't know much about football either, do you? That lad's brilliant, Geoff.

Mr Parker	He must be quite good. City want him in spite of the way he said he played at the trial. Their letter was a very clear offer.
Uncle Ken	And Steve didn't say anything?
Mr Parker	Not a thing. He just read it and dropped it on the table.
Uncle Ken	And Peg?
Mr Parker	She was surprised. I mean – it shook both of us a bit but we had no time to talk this morning. I haven't seen her since. She must have come in, got tea ready and gone out before I came home.
Uncle Ken	Where to?
Mr Parker	I don't know but I think I can hear her at the door now.
Uncle Ken	A firm offer of a place with City. Don't you wonder if you're still doing the right thing?
Mr Parker	I let myself be guided by Peg.

Mrs Parker comes in.

	Hello, love. Where've you been?
Mrs Parker	I've been round to see Steve's PE master.
Uncle Ken	Have you?

Steve comes in.

Steve	I thought I heard Uncle Ken.

He sees his mother. He is about to go.

Mrs Parker	Wait a minute, Steve.
Steve	What do you want?
Mrs Parker	I've just been talking to Mr Brooker. I should have done it before.
Steve	Mr Brooker?
Mrs Parker	He gave me a great deal of his time, so he must have thought you were worth it. He's opened my eyes to a lot of things. He thinks you've a splendid future. I can see now you could have a real career in sport.
Steve	I don't want a career in sport. I want to play football.

Mrs Parker	That, too. Just before I got to his house, he'd had a phone call. A scout from Liverpool must have seen you play. Mr Brooker explained what that could mean
Steve	Liverpool?
Uncle Ken	By heck!
Mrs Parker	So, if your heart's set on playing for a club, we're not set on standing in your way any more.
Mr Parker	Hang on, Peg. This is all a bit sudden, isn't it?
Mrs Parker	You don't agree?
Mr Parker	Well – er – I – yes. Yes. I suppose so.
Steve	I can't believe this.
Mrs Parker	Is that all you can say?
Steve	No. No – thanks, Mum. You won't regret it. I promise you, you won't be sorry.
Mrs Parker	I certainly hope not.
Uncle Ken	You're doing the right thing, Peg.
Mr Parker	But what on earth made you change your mind?
Mrs Parker	It's a long story. Just let me go and hang my coat up. Then I'll tell you.

Keep Taking the Tablets

CAST: **Dad (Mr Moore)**
Mum (Mrs Moore)
Colin
Sarah
Mrs Hanson
Chemist
Mrs Rogers
Doctor

SCENE: *Breakfast time at the Moores'*

Mum Ready for your breakfast, love?
Dad Some breakfast! An ounce of oatflakes and skimmed milk!
Mum You must keep up with your diet. You are losing weight, aren't you?
Dad I know. I know.
Mum Did you weigh yourself this morning?
Dad Yes. I was quite pleased. I've lost nearly another doof.
Mum You what?
Dad Nearly another pound.
Mum You said 'another doof'.
Dad I didn't.
Mum You did. You gave a tiny hiccup and said 'doof'.
Dad I didn't realise. Must have been a slip of the doof.
Mum There. You did it again.
Dad I said 'a slip of the tongue'.
Mum No. You may have meant to say that. You said 'a slip of the doof'.
Dad Does it matter? Give me that bowl of oatflakes.

Colin comes in.

Colin Hey, Dad, I need two pounds.
Dad Two pounds! What for? You're always asking for doof.
Colin Doof?

Dad	I said 'money'. Can't you listen?
Colin	Doof? Is that old slang for money?

Sarah comes in.

Sarah	Is dad in a bad temper again?
Dad	No, I am not in a bad temper! Honestly! I don't know what's the doof with you all this morning.
Mum	There! You're at it again.
Sarah	At what?
Dad	Never you mind. Get on with your doof.
Sarah	My doof? Mum, Dad called my breakfast a 'doof'. How silly.
Dad	Oh do shut up, Sarah!
Colin	Why do you keep using that word, Dad?
Dad	I do not keep using any doof, Colin.
Mum	You do, you know. You've just done it again.
Dad	If you would all stop harping on about it, I'd be doof right.
Mum	What is the doof with you? Look! You've got me doing it.
Dad	I don't know. Probably a touch of doof.
Mum	Of what?
Dad	Indigestion.
Mum	Well, you'd better pop into the chemist's on the way to work.
Dad	All right. All right. I'd better be off. Doof at the time.
Colin	I wish you'd stop saying that, Dad.
Sarah	So do I.
Mum	Yes. Can't you control it? It sounds so doof.
Dad	You said 'doof' then.
Mum	I doof. It's your fault. You started me off.
Dad	That's right! Doof me for everything!
Mum	Stop it. If you get some tablets from the chemist, doof some back for me.

SCENE:	*In the street*

Mrs Hanson	Good morning, Mr Moore.
Dad	Morning. Lovely doof.
Mrs Hanson	I beg your pardon.
Dad	I doof – sorry – said, 'Lovely day.'

Mrs Hanson	You poor man.
Dad	Eh?
Mrs Hanson	I never realised before. You have trouble with your speech.
Dad	It's nothing to doof – worry – about.
Mrs Hanson	Don't be ashamed. I can help you.
Dad	I can help myself, thanks. I'm going to the chemist and then I have to doof off to work.
Mrs Hanson	You can't go to work like that. I was like you once – a prey to every illness going.
Dad	I'm not doof. I'm not ill.
Mrs Hanson	Then I read a wonderful book – 'Mahatma's Mind Control'. It taught me that all illness is in the mind.
Dad	Can we doof this until another time, Mrs Hanson?
Mrs Hanson	No illness can attack me because my mind is doof.
Dad	You mean 'strong'.
Mrs Hanson	I said 'strong'. If your mind is strong, then you are doof.
Dad	Lord! It's catching.
Mrs Hanson	Don't give in, Mr Moore. Be doof. Oh dear! What's the doof with me?
Dad	Indigestion, Mrs Hanson?
Mrs Hanson	You think so, Mr Doof? I'd better go home and read my doof again.

SCENE: *The chemists'*

Chemist	Good morning, sir. Can I doof – help you?
Dad	I hope so. I want some doof – tablets.
Chemist	Are you doof – mocking me?
Dad	Doof.
Chemist	You're doof – doing it again. You're not doof – not funny, you know.
Dad	I'm not trying to be doof – funny. It doof – started this morning.
Chemist	Cut that doof business out. Tell me what you really doof – want.
Dad	You've doof it too, have you?
Chemist	I'm getting a bit doof – sick of this.
Dad	I'm not doof – I'm not making doof – fun of you. I keep doof – going doof. Doof! I want

	some doof – some tablets for doof.
Chemist	Tablets! I haven't got any doof – tablets. Do you think if I doof any tablets for it, I'd be doof – going doof like this.
Dad	No doof! Well, what am I going to doof?
Chemist	How the doof do I doof?
Dad	I can't doof on like this.
Chemist	How do you think I doof?
Dad	I doof I'd better doof a doof.
Chemist	Doof?
Dad	A doof – a doof – a doctor.
Chemist	That's a good doof. Hang on. I'll lock up the doof and doof with you.

SCENE:	*The doctor's waiting room*

Dad	How long have we doof waiting here?
Chemist	Too doof long.
Dad	I'm doof – getting worse.
Chemist	Doof am I.
Dad	Go and doof the receptionist.
Chemist	Right. Come doof. We'll both doof.

They go to the desk.

Dad	Excuse me.
Mrs Rogers	Yes?
Chemist	How long are we doof to be doof waiting here?
Mrs Rogers	What did you say?
Dad	He said, 'How doof are we going to be kept doof here?'
Mrs Rogers	I'm sorry?
Chemist	He doof, 'Doof long are we doof to be doof doof here?'
Mrs Rogers	How long?
Chemist	Doof.
Mrs Rogers	What?
Dad	How long doof – waiting?
Mrs Rogers	Ah! I see. Not long now. The doctor's nearly finished with his last patient.
Chemist	We've been doof about a long doof.
Mrs Rogers	I didn't quite catch that.
Dad	He said, 'We've been hanging doof a doof doof.'
Mrs Rogers	Pardon?

Doctor	*(on intercom)* You can send the next patient in now, Mrs Rogers.
Mrs Rogers	Good. The doctor's ready. He'll see you now.
Chemist	About doof time!
Dad	We'll doof in together.

SCENE: *The doctor's surgery*

Doctor	You're together?
Chemist	Doof.
Doctor	Ah! Is this what I think it is?
Chemist	I don't doof. What the doof doof do you think it is?
Doctor	Have a cream bun. ·
Dad	Doof?
Doctor	Go on. Take one.
Dad	Have you gone doof?
Chemist	I don't want a doof cream bun. I want some doof help. So you can doof your cream buns.
Doctor	Calm down. You'll find it can help.
Dad	I can't eat doof doof. I'm on a doof.
Doctor	I thought so. A diet. I was on a diet but I've given it up. Being on a diet is part of your trouble. Have a cream bun.
Chemist	Oh, doof right.

He takes a cream bun from the bag and starts to eat.

Dad	No, doof.
Doctor	Eat one. It'll do you good. I'm going to have one.

He takes a cream bun and then speaks into the intercom.

Mrs Rogers.

Mrs Rogers	*(on intercom).* Yes, doctor?
Doctor	Send out for another dozen cream buns, will you?
Mrs Rogers	*(on intercom)* Right away, doctor.
Doctor	You both have a virus. There's a lot of it about. I imagine you're both dieting.
Chemist	I am.

Dad	Doof.
Doctor	Hmm. The virus attacks the speech centres and dieting makes it worse.
Chemist	I'm not doof what causes it. Can you doof it?
Doctor	I think so. The first thing is to stop dieting.
Dad	Thank doof for that.
Chemist	You can doof that again. I hated that doof doof.
Doctor	Plenty of rich foods. Those cream buns are helping, aren't they?
Chemist	They are. Can I doof another?
Doctor	Certainly. Here you are.
Dad	Anything doof?
Doctor	Yes. Here are some new tablets just on the market. I'll give you those.
Dad	Thanks very doof.
Doctor	And here are yours. Take three a day and both of you come back and see me in a week.
Chemist	Are they any doof – good?
Doctor	Oh, yes. Three a day, remember.
Dad	Thank you, doctor.
Doctor	Good morning.

Dad and the chemist go out.

Doctor	*(over intercom)* Mrs Rogers, when you bring in the cream buns, bring me in another bottle of those Contradoof pills, please.
Mrs Rogers	Another bottle? How many of them have *you* taken this morning, doctor?
Doctor	Never you mind, Mrs Rogers. I need them. Patients must have confidence in their doctor.
Mrs Rogers	And all those cream buns.
Doctor	I haven't eaten them all myself.
Mrs Rogers	The girl's just brought the new lot. That's forty eight you've had in there this morning.
Doctor	I'm the doctor and that's my business. So that's enough Mrs Doof. Send the next doof in, please.

Tom's Fantasy

CAST:
Headmaster
Tom
Mrs Murgatroyd
Mr Silvester
Alison Denham
Julian Oxmoor
Mr Cole
Joey Dare
Tim
Pippa

SCENE: *The Head's room*

Tom knocks at the door.

Head   Come in. Ah, Tom. Nice to see you.

Tom   You sent for me, sir.

Head   Yes, I certainly did. I'd like you to meet Mrs Murgatroyd. She is the Chairperson of the Governors.

Mrs M   Pleased to meet you, Tom.

Tom   Is it that bad, sir? Am I to be expelled?

Head   Certainly not. In fact, quite the reverse.

Tom   You mean I'm not to be expelled?

Mrs M   You're to be made Headteacher, Tom. The Governors made the decision last night. Are you shocked?

Tom   Well, slightly surprised, I suppose. But I think I can handle it okay.

Head   You see, Tom, I'm no longer a young man.

Tom   You're rather an old one, sir.

Head   Yes, you're quite right. Things have been getting on top of me recently. There has been a lot of fighting, smoking and general misbehaviour in the school recently, as you well know.

Tom   I'll stamp it out. No bother.

Head   Well, of course, you've been doing a large part of it yourself, so we thought if we made you Head, much of it would stop overnight.

Tom	What's happening to you, sir?
Mrs M	The Head's going to take a year off, Tom. He'll return after a year and then the Governors will decide between you and him as the permanent Headteacher.
Head	May the better man win, Tom.
Tom	I'm sure he will, sir. And I hope you won't be too disappointed.
Mrs M	When do you think you could start, Tom?
Tom	Well, I think tomorrow would be best. I'll be able to miss Physics, won't I?
Head	Oh yes, Tom. You won't have any time for lessons, I'm afraid.
Tom	Don't worry about it, sir.
Head	Call me Arthur, Tom.
Tom	Arthur, is it? We always guessed the 'A' stood for Alfred or Angus.
Mrs M	Well, Tom, I must be off. If there are any difficulties, don't hesitate to get in touch.
Tom	I don't anticipate any trouble.
Head	I'll make the annoucement that you've been made Head at assembly tomorrow, Tom.
Tom	Call me Head, Arthur.

SCENE: *The Head's room – next morning*

Tom is sitting in his office. There is a knock at the door.

Tom	Come in.

Mr Silvester comes in.

	Ah, Mr Silvester. Just stand there a moment while I finish this apple. Can't talk while we're eating, can we, Mr Silvester?
Mr S	No, sir.
Tom	I wanted to have a word with you about certain reports you've written.
Mr S	Anything wrong?
Tom	Almost everything. There's one in particular that is absolutely diabolical.
Mr S	Maybe it's a diabolical child I was writing about.

Tom	It certainly wasn't. Do you remember when I was a pupil in your class, Mr Silvester?
Mr S	Quite clearly, Head. It was yesterday at half past two.
Tom	Would you care to read this report?

He hands over his report to Mr Silvester.

Mr S	'English: Tom must try to . . . .'
Tom	No, go straight to the Maths column, Mr Silvester, if you don't mind.
Mr S	'If Tom does not improve on his abysmal efforts, the only thing he is ever likely to pass is water.'
Tom	Would you care to explain yourself, Mr Silvester? Was that your idea of a joke?
Mr S	Well, it was a joke, I suppose, sir, but you must admit . . . .
Tom	I admit nothing, Silvester. Do you realise you were dealing with a most sensitive child? You might have damaged him for life.
Mr S	You don't look very damaged, sir.
Tom	That's because I can rise above it – like I've risen above you.
Mr S	That's something I don't understand. The Governors must be mad.
Tom	No, it's you that's mad, Silvester. I've seen you jumping around in rages and insulting the poor pupils. How would you like to be insulted? What if I were to say your trousers are way out of fashion, your jacket from a jumble sale and your hairstyle simply ridiculous? Get yourself some new gear, Silvester, and have a mohican or a flat-top – look a bit with it, guy.
Mr S	I cannot afford new clothes on a teacher's salary, sir.
Tom	Look, Silvester. I'm not an unreasonable chap. I'll ask my secretary to slip you a few quid out of the petty cash.
Mr S	Thank you, sir.
Tom	Don't mention it, Silvo. But you must smarten yourself up, stop bullying the children and stop writing insulting reports. Now buzz off;

I've a lot to do.

Mr S Right, sir. Thank you.

Tom Oh, and Silvester . . . .

Mr S Yes, sir?

Tom Don't throw chalk at the pupils. We're not made of money, you know.

SCENE: *The same – a little later*

Tom is sitting at his desk, smoking a cigar. Alison Denham and Julian Oxmoor come in.

Tom Ah, come in, Ali. You must wait outside, Oxmoor. I'll see you later.

Julian You asked to see us both.

Tom But not together. I just didn't want to waste my time sending for you. So off you toddle.

Julian I've got an important lesson to go to.

Tom Just you wait outside and do as you're told, unless you want to be in detention.

Julian goes out, very annoyed.

Now Ali, I've been wanting a word with you for some time.

Alison Yes, sir?

Tom What is your relationship with that boy?

Alison It's private, sir.

Tom I need to know everything that goes on in my school.

Alison He's my boyfriend, you know that.

Tom Do you realise he has a spotty face, very thin legs and knobbly knees?

Alison He's not that bad. Anyway, I like him.

Tom What is there to like about him?

Alison He's friendly and funny.

Tom Have you seen him playing football? Totally useless.

Alison I don't mind that. Anyway, you're not so good yourself.

Tom I'm in the team.

Alison You're not.

Tom You look on the list on the notice board. I'm striker on Saturday.

Alison	The Head can't play in the Under 14s.
Tom	Why not? I'm only 13.
Alison	You made Mr Cippard put you in, I bet.
Tom	I persuaded him. I'm afraid he doesn't know the first thing about football. I'm thinking of getting rid of him. Still, I admit that he understood the error of his ways, when I pointed out to him how good I was. I hope you'll do the same.
Alison	What errors have I made?
Tom	Julian Oxmoor. Get rid of him.
Alison	Why should I?
Tom	He's totally unsuitable. He's useless.
Alison	He's good at Maths and Physics.
Tom	He won't be soon.
Alison	And why not?
Tom	I'm abolishing them. They're both off the timetable from next week. There'll be more football instead.
Alison	And why is it that you're so keen for me to get rid of Julian?
Tom	You're wasted on him. You need a bright, good-looking lad . . . .
Alison	Like you, for instance.
Tom	That's right.
Alison	How could I go out with the Headmaster?
Tom	Quite easy. You could be the Headmistress.
Alison	And what about Miss Jonson?
Tom	She's retiring. She told me this morning. Anyway, she was far too old.
Alison	Would I be able to miss lessons and sit in Miss Jonson's office?
Tom	Of course. And you could be in the hockey team.
Alison	I don't think I'm good enough.
Tom	You will be. Just wait till I've had a word with Mrs Moore.
Alison	I'd feel sorry for Julian.
Tom	Don't worry about him. I'll make him a prefect, if he behaves himself.
Alison	I hope he won't mind.
Tom	Of course he won't. How about going to see 'The Ghoul of Gorton' tonight?

Alison	I've heard it's good; I don't think I could afford . . . .
Tom	Don't be silly. I'll take a few quid out of the Head's Fund. See you six thirty outside the Regal.
Alison	I'd better tell Julian.
Tom	Don't worry. I'll tell him myself. Send him in.

SCENE: *The same – an hour or so later*

Tom is interviewing Mr Cole, the English teacher.

Tom	Now, I'm willing to let you stay on, Mr Cole, as long as you change your ways.
Mr Cole	And what ways should I change, Headmaster?
Tom	Mr Cole, I'd like to ask you a simple question: 'What have you been doing with your fourth year class this morning?'
Mr Cole	We were reading 'David Copperfield'.
Tom	And who's this Copperfield when he's at home?
Mr Cole	It's a novel by Dickens, Head.
Tom	So you admit it?
Mr Cole	Admit what?
Tom	That you're still reading books by dead people. There's that other one I warned you against – Julian Caesar. I've had a young boy in here half an hour ago telling me you've been upsetting his class by reading him.
Mr Cole	It's their play for the exams. 'Julius Caesar', by Shakespeare, in case you didn't know, Head.
Tom	Oh, I know him – Shakespeare. I know him all right, Mr Cole. He's dead, that's what he is.
Mr Cole	About three hundred years dead. What's your point, Head?
Tom	Haven't you heard the expression 'Dead men tell no tales', Mr Cole?
Mr Cole	Certainly, Head. The expression means, as far as I understand it . . . .
Tom	That's the point. You don't understand much, Mr Cole. Now, have you read this?

He hands over a book.

Mr Cole	'Revenge of the Three-eyed Werewolf' – no, I don't believe I have.
Tom	Well, you'd better get it read quick. I've ordered 300 copies for the fourth year. You'll start reading it with them on Monday.
Mr Cole	It doesn't appear to be a work of much literary merit, Head.
Tom	Don't you worry your head about that, Mr Cole. It's a good one, you take my word for it. Twenty three murders in the first thirty pages.
Mr Cole	Charming.
Tom	I'm glad you think so. Now don't let me hear of you boring the children with that Dicknews and Shakespain rubbish again.

Joey Dare comes in.

Joey	Hi, Tom. I got your call.
Tom	Great to see you, Joey. When can you start?
Joey	Any time, guy. You name it.
Tom	Okay, tomorrow at nine sharpish. I just need to give that old square her marching orders.
Mr Cole	Excuse me, Head. Who is this person, and who, if you don't mind my asking, is the 'old square'?
Tom	It just proves what I've been saying about you, Mr Cole. You're out of touch. This is Joey Dare, lead singer of Diminished Responsibility. He's the new music master.
Mr Cole	But what about Miss Thomas?
Tom	She's the old square I'm getting rid of. I've just sent Ali to confiscate those boring records she used to play to me. We're burning them at dinner time.

SCENE:	*The same – the following Monday*

Tom and Alison are sitting. Tom has his leg in plaster.

Alison	You needn't keep moaning like that. I've got a bruise the size of a saucer on my bottom.
Tom	Why did they do it, Ali?

Alison	They hate you, that's why.
Tom	But we were on the same side. I mean you expect your opponents to tackle you, but not your own side. They all jumped at me as soon as I got the ball. I'll expel them all.
Alison	You can't. They were just playing football, they'll say.
Tom	Foot-Tom more like. Who bashed you?
Alison	I never saw her. I just felt a terrible shooting pain from behind. I think it was Jenny.
Tom	She's your best friend.
Alison	Not now I'm Headmistress, she isn't. She hates me.

Two first years, Tim and Pippa, come in.

Tom	What do you want?
Pippa	We were sent.
Tim	By Miss Lawson.
Pippa	For holding hands.
Tim	In Geography.
Pippa	Like you two were doing.
Tim	And worse.
Pippa	In the pictures.
Tim	Last Saturday.
Pippa	We saw you.
Tim	So there.
Pippa	We've told our Mums.
Tim	They're coming up.
Pippa	To sort you out.
Tim	So we're off now.
Pippa	We've seen you.
Tim	Like Miss Lawson said.
Pippa	We'll do it again.
Tim	And you can't stop us.

They go out.

Tom	Hey, come back. Ali, fetch them back.
Alison	Fetch them yourself.
Tom	You know I can't walk.
Alison	I've made a decision.
Tom	What's that?
Alison	I'm resigning.

Tom	You can't. I need you.
Alison	I'm fed up with being Headmistress. Julian said he'd have me back if I resigned.
Tom	Go on, then. Get out. I'll manage, don't you worry.
Alison	Best of luck, sir.

She goes out as Mrs Murgatroyd comes in.

Tom	Oh, hello. Sit down. You look tired.
Mrs M	Tired! I'll say I'm tired. I've been badgered all weekend by parents ringing me up.
Tom	No complaints, I trust.
Mrs M	No complaints! The school's gone mad. Mr Silvester has a mohican haircut and an awful striped suit; the English teacher's reading filthy books; there have been complaints about you and the Headmistress's behaviour last Saturday; and there's seventeen pounds missing from the petty cash.
Tom	I can explain all this.
Mrs M	Try explaining it to the policeman. He's next door talking to your secretary. What have you to say for yourself?
Tom	I'm resigning. That's what. I'm going back to 4B.
Mrs M	Too late. They'd kick your other leg in. The most likely place for you to go is prison.
Tom	You can't prove anything against me.
Mrs M	Can't we? There's a queue of willing witnesses against you, headed by Alison Denham.

Julian Oxmoor comes in.

Julian	Excuse me, sir. I've been sent to ask you to come and have a word with Sergeant Brown. I'll help you up. Oh, what a pity! I just caught your plaster with my foot. Never mind, I'm sure you'll be able to give your leg a good long rest where you're going.

The Strange Girl

CAST:	**Miss Searson** **Keri** **Cheryl** **Samantha** **Mary** **Headmistress**
SCENE:	*Maybury Comprehensive School, 4G's classroom – at the end of a lesson*

Miss S	Keri, Cheryl, Samantha, come here a minute, please.
Keri	Right, Miss.
Cheryl	Okay, Miss.
Samantha	Coming, Miss.
Miss S	This is Mary. She's a stranger to the school and to the area as well. Help her round school today, please.
Cheryl	Okay, Miss, leave it to us.
Keri	We'll tell her all about the teachers, Miss – the good ones and the bad ones.
Miss S	No doubt you will.
Samantha	Hello, Mary.
Mary	Hello.
Samantha	Where you come from then?
Mary	Up North.
Cheryl	You can tell by the accent.
Mary	Can you?
Cheryl	Do you support Liverpool?
Mary	I don't come from Liverpool.
Cheryl	But you could support them.
Mary	Support?
Cheryl	The football team.
Mary	Oh, no, I'm not much of a one for games.
Samantha	We could take you down West Ham.
Mary	Shopping?
Samantha	No, the football team.
Mary	Will there be many people there?
Samantha	Crowds.

Mary	I'd like that.
Keri	Come on, we'll be late for Maths.

SCENE: *Outside the school – at the end of the school day*

Keri	She's odd, isn't she?
Cheryl	She never said a word in class.
Keri	She's no idea about pop records.
Samantha	Perhaps it's because of her first day. I bet I'd be shy, if they sent me up North.
Keri	Where's she living?
Cheryl	She didn't seem sure. From the way she described it I bet it's the Walton Court flats.
Keri	Shouldn't we have seen her home?
Samantha	She dashed off too fast. She may not be much of a one for games but she can certainly run.

SCENE: 4G's classroom – next day

Samantha	What time did the Chinaman go to the dentist?
Mary	I don't know.
Samantha	Two thirty.
Mary	Two thirty?
Samantha	Tooth hurt-ee. D'you get it?
Mary	He was in pain?
Samantha	It's a joke.
Mary	I understand. A joke.
Cheryl	What do you think of Miss Searson, our form teacher?
Mary	She's nice.
Keri	Wasn't Geography boring today?
Mary	I find it interesting. I like to learn about the Earth.
Keri	Rather you than me.
Cheryl	Do you like boys?
Mary	Boys are nice.
Cheryl	Keri's going out with Nigel.
Keri	Shut up!
Mary	Is she?
Cheryl	Did you go out with a boy up North?
Mary	Oh, yes.
Cheryl	Tell us about him.
Mary	It is difficult.

Cheryl	What did he look like?
Mary	He was tall.
Samantha	What else?
Mary	Oh, it is difficult to describe him.
Keri	You are a one. Have you a photo?
Mary	No, I've no photo.
Keri	Will you write to him?
Mary	Write? I expect so.
Cheryl	The boys in this class are rubbish.
Keri	You!
Cheryl	Except for Nigel, of course.
Keri	Shut up!

SCENE: *In the road outside – after school*

Keri	There she goes!
Cheryl	Call her!
Samantha	Mary! Mary! Wait for us!
Keri	She can't hear us.
Cheryl	She's gone round the corner. Run!

They run round the corner.

	She's gone.
Samantha	She's disappeared into thin air.
Keri	She must have run like a train. There are no paths off.
Cheryl	How odd.

SCENE: *The Headmistress's study*

Head	How is Mary Smith getting on?
Miss S	She is very shy.
Head	Have the girls been friendly to her?
Miss S	Oh, yes. I put her with Cheryl, Keri and Samantha.
Head	Do you think she is happy?
Miss S	She never shows it if she is. It's hard to understand her.
Head	What about her work?
Miss S	Other teachers' reports show there is a lot she does not know. I would describe her knowledge as . . . . as . . . .
Head	Go on.

Miss S	Well, it seems old-fashioned and out of date. There must be some rum schools up North.
Head	Has she a uniform yet?
Miss S	Not yet.
Head	Is she in the right class?
Miss S	I should leave her where she is for the time being. I have this feeling she might run off, if we press her too hard.

SCENE: *The school yard*

Cheryl	We tried to walk home with you last night.
Mary	Oh.
Keri	You must have run like the wind. You went round the corner and disappeared.
Mary	My father picked me up in his car.
Samantha	Oh.

The school bell rings.

Mary	There goes the bell.

She runs off.

Samantha	Just a minute.
Keri	What?
Samantha	No car passed us. And there's only one way out of that street.
Cheryl	It must have done. Why should she lie to us?
Keri	She doesn't exactly lie, but you feel she is not telling the truth all the time.
Cheryl	Come on.

SCENE: *In the road outside – after school*

Cheryl	There she goes.
Samantha	Shall we go after her?
Keri	No, we must talk. I've noticed something.
Samantha	What?
Keri	Well, when Mr Jackson made his jokes in history she didn't laugh once. The rest of the class was laughing.
Cheryl	Perhaps she has no sense of humour.

Samantha	She didn't understand the joke about the Chinaman.
Keri	And when in RE Miss Hollingsworth told us about those handicapped children, the girls were all crying – but not her.
Samantha	I did.
Cheryl	So did I.
Keri	Her eyes were quite clear. I just don't think she has the normal human emotions.
Samantha	She has that fixed expression.
Cheryl	Well, she is human. She talks like one. She breathes. I think she's just odd and hasn't settled down in London.
Keri	She could be more odd than you think.
Samantha	Why do you say that?
Keri	I just have this feeling.

SCENE: *In class – next day, at the end of a lesson*

Miss S	Ah, I wanted to have a chat with you, Mary. Samantha, Cheryl, Keri – stick around, you may be able to help. *(to Mary)* Some of the teachers say you are having difficulties with some of the subjects.
Mary	I do my best, Miss. I'm learning all the time.
Miss S	I wondered if . . . . look out!

Part of the ceiling falls down over Mary. The other girls shriek.

Miss S	It's covered Mary. Mary, are you all right?
Keri	Mary!
Miss S	Quick, pull that heavy piece of plaster off her. Mary, how are you?
Mary	I'm all right.
Miss S	You took a terrific knock.
Samantha	Mary, love.
Miss S	Don't try to get up.
Mary	I'm all right. Don't fuss.
Miss S	You must see a doctor.
Mary	No, I don't want to see a doctor.
Miss S	How are you other girls?
Keri	Just the shock. The ceiling missed us.

Miss S These old schools. They can be death traps.
Don't move, Mary. We'll get help.

Mary No, I'm going home.

She gets up and runs out.

Miss S Mary, come back! Oh, do stop her. I must make
a report about this. Stop her, please.

SCENE: *In class – next morning*

Keri It was just the same, Miss. When we went
round the corner she had disappeared. There
was no car to pick her up.

Miss S Is she in yet? The Head wants to see her. She
must be examined by a doctor.

Cheryl We haven't seen her this morning.

Miss S As soon as you do send her to me.

Samantha We'll look if you like.

Miss S No, go to your lessons.

SCENE: *The Head's study*

Head It's most odd. I tried to phone her parents last
night and I find out the address she gave us
does not exist.

Miss S When you interviewed her when she came to
the school were her parents with her?

Head No, she said they were both working. She
brought a letter and said she was from up
North – Bradford way. I have it here.

Miss S That's her handwriting.

Head Precisely.

Miss S Oh.

Head I then contacted the school in the letter and
what do you think?

Miss S What?

Head They've no recent pupil called Mary Smith.

Miss S She gave us a false name. What's the mystery
of that I wonder?

Head The mystery is, Miss Searson, that they had a
girl called Mary Smith five years ago and she
was killed in this area with her parents in a
car crash.

Miss S Good heavens!
Head Say nothing to the pupils.
Miss S Of course.

SCENE: *The classroom – later*

Cheryl I wonder why Miss Searson won't say nothing?
Samantha I saw the police coming out of the Head's office.
Cheryl I reckon she's bunked off.
Keri I have a feeling she was not real.
Cheryl How do you mean?
Keri Did you ever touch her?
Cheryl No.
Keri I did. I held her hand. It was dead cold.
Samantha So she had bad circulation.
Keri I think it was more than that. She was not a real person.
Cheryl That's your imagination. She's just a lonely kid who has bunked off.
Samantha Come, let's get some crisps from the tuck shop. Forget about her for the moment!
Keri I could never forget about her. Never.

The Pond

CAST:	**Mrs Eldon**
	Bob ⎫
	Colin ⎬ Mrs Eldon's children
	Sue ⎭
	Stannard
	Yorky
	Police sergeant

SCENE: *A disused quarry in rough woodland, now used as an unofficial dump*

Bob pushes a wheelbarrow to the edge. Colin and Sue are with him.

Bob Here we are, kids.

Colin What exactly are we getting?

Bob You'll see. Leave the barrow there. Come on.

Sue Down in the dump? We'll get filthy, slithering down there.

Bob No. Just down this bank.

He scrambles down. Colin and Sue follow. He shows them a hole.

Colin Are those tiles in there?

Bob They're small slabs of some metal.

Sue Why are they painted white? What are they for?

Bob How should I know? Grab hold.

He reaches and pulls one of the metal slabs out and gives it to Colin.

Colin Hey! This is heavy.

Bob It needs to be.

Sue How many are there?

Bob I don't know. Say twenty – maybe thirty.

Colin Thirty! You mean we've got to carry thirty of these flipping things?

Bob Only up the bank.

Sue takes one.

Sue   They *are* heavy. What do you want all these for?

Bob   Look! Stop nattering on. Let's get on with it.

Sue   It's stealing, taking stuff like this.

Bob   Is it heck! They've been thrown away.

Colin   I don't think you know what you're doing.

Bob   Of course I do. I'm going to line that hole we dug with a thick sheet of plastic and weight down the edges with these.

Colin   I'd just drop that plastic pool-shape into the hole.

Bob   Oh yes, you would, wouldn't you? Then, if it got a crack in it, all the water would run out.

Colin   It wouldn't.

Bob   I'm telling you, it would.

Sue   Why can't you weigh the plastic sheet down with stones?

Bob   Because I don't want to. I want these. They're ideal. Look, do you want to help me or not?

Colin   No.

Sue   We didn't know these things would be so heavy.

Bob   Listen! Mum's going to have that ornamental pool for her birthday. She's expecting it. She's promised not to go near the place until it's ready. You two promised to help. You wanted to help. I need your help. Are you going to help or not?

Sue   We didn't know you wanted to cart sogging great lumps of metal for miles and miles.

Bob   All right! All right! Go home! I'll do it all on my own. If you don't care about giving Mum a bit of pleasure—!

Colin   Well—

Sue   Why on earth do you want all of them?

Bob   One or two won't do. I want the lot. They'll make a nice flat surround. A good base.

Colin   They're not iron because they're not rusty. See where the paint's flaked off this one.

Bob   They must all have been covered up with soil at first. I only spotted them when that heavy rain washed some of it away.

Colin	If we went home and got a bag, we could put one or two in it and drag it up the bank with a rope.
Bob	You're just wasting time, aren't you? Right! I dug them all out, I can carry them all home. Get out of my way!

Bob picks up one of the small metal slabs and begins to carry it up the bank. Colin follows him, carrying another slab.

Colin	Like carrying a sack of spuds.
Sue	We won't get all these in the barrow. They'll weigh a ton.
Bob	We'll make several trips. Come on.
Sue	All right! All right!

She goes up the bank with another slab.

SCENE: *The same spot – very early the following morning*

It is dark. Stannard and Yorky stand by the 'dump', looking down.

Yorky	I could have broken an axle on that truck along that farm road.
Stannard	Stop ruddy moaning.
Yorky	It'll be worse going out with all that weight.
Stannard	We'll manage. They're just down there, I think. Shine the light.
Yorky	I can't see anything.
Stannard	You could have brought a better torch. Anyway, you wouldn't see anything. They're buried. They'll be easy enough to spot when we dig 'em out. They're painted white.
Yorky	What for?
Stannard	So they don't look like what they are, naturally. After the snatch at the airport, Kenny decided to hide his share all over the place. It couldn't travel as it was so he painted it all white.
Yorky	Hmm. Funny.
Stannard	Not funny, smart. Hand me that spade.

He begins to scramble down the bank followed by Yorky.

Yorky It's taking it to the coast on Friday night that's got me bothered.

Stannard Why? It's been moved about already on the backs of lorries. No one's spotted it. You'll be driving what looks like a small load of white tiles. No one's going to stop you. Hey! It can't be!

Yorky What?

Stannard It's not here. There's just a hole. Unless . . . . Shine your light. Not there. Higher.

Yorky There?

Stannard Yes. Stop. I buried it in line with that tree. This is the right place. Well, I'll be . . . . It's been nicked!

Yorky Nicked? Are you sure?

Stannard Of course, I'm sure, you prat!

York But who could have nicked it? Who knew about it? One of Morrie's lot?

Stannard No. They didn't know it was here.

Yorky Who did?

Stannard Only me.

Yorky What if someone followed you? Saw you plant it?

Stannard Do me a favour. Followed me? No one followed me. I saw to that.

Yorky What's Kenny going to say?

Stannard It's not what he'll say. It's what he'll do.

Yorky Not to me he won't. You're the one who hid it.

Stannard Oh yes? And what if he gets the idea we're lying and have nicked the stuff ourselves?

Yorky I'll tell him.

Stannard Tell him? Tell him while he's doing his nut? He won't listen. You know Kenny Walsh. He'll go berserk. No. You're in this with me.

Yorky Cripes, mate! What are we going to do?

Stannard How the hell do I know?

Yorky Maybe they've slipped out of the hole and dropped further down the quarry. Look! Are they there where I'm shining the torch? .

Stannard No they are not, you cloth-headed lunatic! They've gone.

Yorky	We'll just have to talk to Kenny. Make him believe us.
Stannard	Look! Footprints – going up from here. Let's get back up the bank. Give me the torch.

They both go back up the bank. Stannard shines the torch round.

Yorky	They'd have to carry them away somehow. You wouldn't get a car this close.
Stannard	You'd get a wheelbarrow. See!
Yorky	Where?
Stannard	There, you dummy. Ruts. Lots of 'em. Churning up the mud.
Yorky	Maybe someone dumping rubbish.
Stannard	Maybe not. They've made more than one trip. Maybe someone taking those ingots away. Come on. Whoever it was, he's left a good clear track.

SCENE: *Mrs Eldon's bedroom – slightly later*

Mrs Eldon is in bed in the dark.

Mrs Eldon	What? What's the matter?
Colin	Mum! Wake up.
Mrs Eldon	Colin! What do you want? Do you know what time it is?
Sue	There's someone outside.
Mrs Eldon	Put the light on. What's all this about?
Sue	I heard a noise and got up to look.
Colin	Yes. She came and woke me.
Sue	I saw the shed door move.
Mrs Eldon	Has one of you left that shed door open again?

Bob comes in.

Bob	What's up? Someone ill?
Mrs Eldon	No. Go back to bed. Sue's had a dream or something.
Bob	A dream? Do you know it's four o'clock in the morning?
Sue	What are you talking about? I haven't had a dream!

Mrs Eldon	She thinks she saw the shed door move.
Bob	Probably the wind. You must have left it open, Colin.
Colin	Why me? You were in there putting back the stuff you'd used working on the pond.
Bob	I closed it, our kid. You put your bike away last. You go down and close it.
Colin	No fear.
Sue	I think there's someone in there. I thought I saw a light flickering.
Bob	Get away. I'll go.
Mrs Eldon	No. Wait a bit. Get your dressing gowns on. We'll all go.

SCENE: *The Eldons' house – next afternoon*

Mrs Eldon opens the front door. Stannard is there.

Stannard	Good afternoon. Department of Health. We're making some house-to-house enquiries. Can you help us?
Mrs Eldon	Yes?
Stannard	There's an old quarry in those woods at the back of these houses. Has anyone from here been up there recently. Your husband?
Mrs Eldon	He's not at home. He's working abroad. What's it all about?
Stannard	Some dangerous waste was dumped in that quarry, quite illegally. When we went to recover it, it had disappeared.
Mrs Eldon	What does it look like?
Stannard	Small white-painted objects.
Mrs Eldon	No. I don't know anything about that.
Stannard	Someone from one of these houses has been in and out of that wood with a wheelbarrow.
Mrs Eldon	When was this?
Stannard	Last night, night before.
Mrs Eldon	Bob and Colin and Sue did have the wheelbarrow. They're using it to build me a pond.
Stannard	Bob?
Mrs Eldon	My children.
Stannard	Could I see this pond?

Mrs Eldon	Well – it sounds daft. I've promised not to go near it till it's finished. Look – who exactly are you? Shouldn't you have a card or something?
Stannard	Quite right. Just a minute.

He pats his pockets.

Ah! Must have left it in the car with the other stuff. Still – there seems no further reason to trouble you. If there is, I'll be back.

He goes down the path, passing Bob and Sue coming up it.

Sue	Who was that, Mum?
Mrs Eldon	I don't really know.
Bob	What did he want?
Mrs Eldon	He was enquiring about some dangerous waste missing from that dump in the quarry but he seemed – sort of – shifty.
Bob	Dangerous waste?
Mrs Eldon	White objects, he said.
Bob	Oh Lord!
Mrs Eldon	Bob! It wasn't you, was it? Oh, dear. Quick! Run after him and tell him.

Bob runs off.

Sue	*(calling after him)* Told you it was stealing!
Mrs Eldon	You come into the house and tell me all about it.

SCENE:	*The Eldons' back garden – very late at night*

Stannard and Yorky are there.

Yorky	I still don't like it.
Stannard	We've been on the watch outside here for half an hour. Nothing's moved.
Yorky	You can't be sure.
Stannard	Listen! Old fogies in the other two houses. Kids and a wheelbarrow in this. It's got to be this one.
Yorky	What if she rumbled you?

Stannard	I was watching her face. She's no idea of what they've got. We're dealing with kids here. Mugs.

He shines the torch.

Yorky	There's the pond.
Stannard	We know they're not in the shed. They can't be in the house. She'd have seen 'em and said.
Yorky	It doesn't show that they'll be here.

They are both by the pond. Stannard examines it.

Stannard	Shut up! I'm looking. Yes! Yes! Here's one. And another. We've got 'em. Yorky, we're made!

A bright light shines on them both.

Sergeant	Don't move! You're nicked! Both of you.
SCENE:	*The Eldons' living room – evening, a few days later*

Mrs Eldon and her children are talking to the police sergeant.

Sergeant	The silver you found was only a small part of the loot.
Bob	From that airport robbery, Mum.
Sergeant	That's right.
Mrs Eldon	And they'd split it up and hidden it in small amounts everywhere.
Sergeant	Painted white to disguise it. Some in that dump, some in a builder's yard, some buried on waste ground – lots of places. We'd suspected Walsh and a man called Maurice but we had no hard evidence. Now we've got all we want.
Mrs Eldon	You've got the whole gang.
Sergeant	We shall have. Once those two started talking, we were able to pick others up. They're going down like a stack of dominoes.

Mrs Eldon	It was Bob who rang the Department of Health.
Bob	They'd never heard of dangerous waste. That man—
Sergeant	Stannard.
Bob	Yes. He was supposed to be going from house to house. When I went after him, he was already driving away in a car.
Sue	And then, before that, one night I'd seen someone in our shed.
Colin	There was no one there when we looked.
Mre Eldon	But – putting it all together made us suspicious.
Bob	So I rang up about Stannard.
Sue	Then we went and looked at the bars.
Colin	We scraped some paint off.
Bob	I said it looked like silver.
Mrs Eldon	That's when we rang you.
Sue	And it was silver.
Sergeant	Yes. We took a bit of a chance, lying in wait like that, but it came off.
Sue	Will we have to give evidence?
Sergeant	Perhaps.
Colin	Hey! Great!
Mrs Eldon	We've been talking about nothing else since it happened.
Sergeant	That's understandable. I came to express our appreciation again, as I said, Mrs Eldon and – er – um –
Mrs Eldon	Yes?
Sergeant	Well – right off the record – the insurance company did offer a substantial reward for information leading to the recovery of the bullion.
Bob	And we might get it.
Sergeant	Ah! You might get some. I don't want to raise your hopes too much so don't say I said so.
Mrs Eldon	We won't.
Sergeant	Well – I'll be getting along. Goodnight to you all.
Mrs Eldon	I'll show you out.

She goes out with the sergeant.

Colin	A reward, eh?

Sue   We could have a big swimming pool.

Colin   A huge, heated Olympic pool.

Bob   Maybe. But the police have been trampling about and digging out there at the back. Repairs are needed. In the meantime, we are going out to do some more work on Mum's pond.

Sherlock Holmes and the Great Trouser Mystery

CAST:	Narrator
	Sherlock Holmes
	Dr Watson
	Headmistress
	Announcer
	BBC Controller

Narrator	There is more bare flesh in this play than on Page Three. Your teacher should therefore leave the room while you are reading it. Right, to begin. The scene is 221B Baker Street, the residence of Sherlock Holmes, the great detective. He is pacing the room, and beating it too.
Holmes	I feel frustrated, Watson.
Watson	It was losing your last case, Holmes.
Holmes	I knew I should not have flown from Heathrow.
Watson	You always lose your cases there.
Holmes	Stay where you are, Watson.
Watson	Why?
Holmes	Someone is coming up the stairs.
Watson	It's the postman, Holmes. Yes, he's putting the post through the door.
Holmes	I lose more doors that way! Why can't we put it through the letter box?
Watson	It is a big letter, Holmes.
Holmes	Don't open it, Watson!
Watson	You fear a letter bomb?
Holmes	Worse. It could be from the Income Tax. Why is it addressed to First Class Sherlock Holmes?
Watson	Because you are the greatest detective in the world.
Holmes	I know, I heard the Narrator say so. Open it, Watson.
Watson	It's from the Headmistress of St Olave's Comprehensive School.
Holmes	My old school! Is it about the lines I owe her?

Watson No, she says she's coming to see you about a great mystery.

The Headmistress comes in.

Headmistress And here I am.
Holmes How did you get in?
Headmistress The door was ajar.
Holmes A jar of what?
Headmistress Open, you fool!

She hits him on the head with her umbrella.

Holmes Oh! Sorry, Miss.
Headmistress Now then, Holmes, can you explain how all the trousers of my male staff went missing last night?
Watson Somebody took them to wash.

The Headmistress hits Watson on the head with her umbrella.

Headmistress Not every single pair, you fool.
Watson How can you have a single pair? I thought a pair was two.
Headmistress Don't banter words with me, Watson. Can you find the culprits, Holmes? All the children are having to be taught by the mistresses and a Scotsman.
Holmes Can't they buy new trousers?
Headmistress Have you not heard of the trouser famine in North London?
Holmes Trousers are short?
Headmistress No, they are the same size they've always been, but there is not a pair to be had.
Watson Why not eat apples instead?
Headmistress A pair of trousers, you fool! Turn on the radio!
Holmes But it hasn't been invented yet.
Headmistress Neither have half the other things in this play. Switch it on.
Announcer This is BBC Radio Four.
Watson Radio for what?
Announcer Radio for idiots, of course. Here is a news flash.

The shortage of trousers in North London continues to spread. To combat the shortage of trouser cloth the Government have stated that as from midnight all trousers are to be made with one leg only.

Holmes Which leg?

Announcer The right leg.

Holmes But what if you are left-handed?

Announcer What does that matter?

Holmes You won't be able to put your hand in your pocket to buy a packet of fags.

Announcer That is the end of the trouser flash.

Watson Don't you mean news flash?

Announcer No. You should have seen what I saw this morning.

Headmistress It's disgusting. Do something, Holmes.

Holmes Right. Call me a cab, Watson.

Watson You're a cab, Holmes.

Holmes Now we need padlocks.

Watson You want to lock up your pad?

Holmes No, to lock our trousers on, you fool.

Headmistress Good luck, Holmes.

Holmes By gad, I shall need it. We must solve this case before the winter sets in.

Narrator Things were indeed getting serious. Through the absence of men, London was grinding to a halt.

Watson The clouds are gathering, Holmes. It could be snow.

Holmes Those are not ordinary clouds, Watson. Hand me my 'Telegraph'.

Watson Don't you mean telescope?

Holmes No, 'Telegraph'. I want to see the football results. I want to see how many drawers I've got.

Watson My God! Holmes, they are not snow clouds. They are clouds of moths.

Holmes You're sure they are not flies?

Watson No, all the flies have disappeared along with the trousers.

Holmes This is a much bigger plot than I thought. Ring up for two tons of mothballs.

Watson (*on phone*) Hello, hello, hello. Mothball

	factory? What? What? What? Moriarty has bought up all the mothballs!
Holmes	Moriarty, my arch villain. So he is behind it all.
Watson	What can we do, Holmes?
Holmes	Think, Watson. What attracts moths?
Watson	Other moths?
Holmes	No – lights, you fool. To the BBC television studios.
Watson	Why, Holmes?
Holmes	I've got two tickets for 'Top of the Pops'.
Headmistress	Good luck, Holmes. Wave to me.
Holmes	Call me a cab, Watson.
Headmistress	You've done that joke, Holmes. Take two hundred lines!
Narrator	We move to the BBC Television Centre.
Controller	You want me to take the roof off the studio?
Holmes	Yes, then all the moths will be attracted to the 'Top of the Pops' lights. Once inside, we put the roof back on again.
Watson	Brilliant, Holmes.
Holmes	Elementary, my dear Watson.
Controller	But what about the programme?
Holmes	Call it a Moth Ball.
Controller	I like it, Holmes. This could get peak viewing figures.
Holmes	Just sign this contract.
Narrator	And so all the moths in London were trapped and killed. Once more, men could walk the streets in dignity.
Watson	And in crimplene too.
Narrator	Meanwhile back at 221B Baker Street.
Holmes	Get me the Press, Watson.
Watson	Which paper, Holmes?
Holmes	The trouser press, you fool.
Watson	Here you are.
Holmes	Oh gad! It hurts.
Watson	You have to take your trousers off first, Holmes.
Holmes	I think we deserve a holiday, Watson.
Watson	Where shall we go, Holmes?
Holmes	Exmouth.
Watson	Exmouth?

Holmes	Ex-moth. Get it? Ha! Ha!
Watson	I don't get it, Holmes.
Holmes	Then you must go back to school.
Headmistress	He can't do that. I've given the children a holiday. They deserve it after reading this play!

Also by Paul Groves, John Griffin and Nigel Grimshaw:

Steps

– a basic secondary school English course with plenty of variety and lively ideas for learning basic English skills.

Book 1 ISBN 0 582 20145 4
    3 ISBN 0 582 20146 2
    3 ISBN 0 582 20147 0
    4 ISBN 0 582 20148 9

Steps to GCSE Success ISBN 0 582 20676 6

Steps Skills Books

Be a writer ISBN 0 582 21997 3
The alphabet at work ISBN 0 582 21995 7
Write in sentences ISBN 0 582 21996 5

On Your Marks

– a fun and lively approach to learning basic English.

Book 1 ISBN 0 582 21143 3
    2 ISBN 0 582 21144 1
    3 ISBN 0 582 21145 X
    4 ISBN 0 582 21146 8

If you would like to read more plays, try **Star Plays**:

Six Silly Plays Paul Groves ISBN 0 582 24379 3
Eight Even Sillier Plays Paul Groves ISBN 0 582 20634 0
Grange Hill 1 Phil Redmond ISBN 0 582 24382 3
Grange Hill 2 Phil Redmond ISBN 0 582 24385 8
The Weathermonger Jan Mark ISBN 0 582 24380 7
The Ramshackle Company Susan Hill ISBN 0 582 24381 5
Izzy Jan Mark ISBN 0 582 20275 2
Perci Gervase Phinn ISBN 0 582 20636 7
Superhero Lesley Davies ISBN 0 582 20638 3
Interference Jan Mark ISBN 0 582 20637 5
Anancy's Magic P & V Nanton ISBN 0 582 20635 9

Longman Group UK Limited,
*Longman House, Burnt Mill, Harlow,
Essex CM20 2JE, England
and Associated Companies throughout the world.*

First-published 1987
Third impression 1990

*Set in 11/13pt Century Schoolbook, Linotron 202
Produced by Longman Singapore Publishers Pte Ltd
Printed in Singapore*

ISBN 0 582 20689 8